C000146242

Report of the
British Geological Survey
1996–97

The mission of the BGS is to contribute to the economic competitiveness of the UK; the effectiveness of public services and policy, including international policy; and the quality of life, by providing the best, most relevant and most up-to-date geoscience information and advice for the United Kingdom, both onshore and offshore, and internationally.

Natural Environment Research Council

Contents

Bill Greenhough

Dr Peter Cook CBE celebrates receiving the Investors in People *standard on behalf of the BGS from the Greater Nottingham Training and Enterprise Council (GNTEC).*

T P Cullen

A sample of porphyritic basalt from the Galapagos Islands collected by Charles Darwin, one of the more exotic items in the BGS Petrological Collection, now in the Britrocks Database. It is often forgotten that Darwin was a geologist by training.

T P Cullen

During her visit to Keyworth, HRH The Princess Royal was introduced to the BGS's programme of national and international geological map production by Dr Chris Green, BGS Publications Manager (left). Carole Mawer is pointing out to the Princess and Prof John Crebs, Chief Executive of the NERC, that Gatcombe Park, the Princess's home, appears on the Cirencester 1:50 000 sheet, which is currently in production.

Director's Introduction

This Annual Report is a notable one for me personally in that I shall be stepping down as Director in January 1998, and this, my eighth BGS Annual Report, will also be my last.

Since I became Director in early 1990 there have been many changes to the Survey as it has responded to new initiatives, new priorities, the changing needs of government and a range of reviews. Some of these reviews have been very helpful; others less so, but throughout them, the BGS has produced more good science and more products for more customers than ever before. For example, the fifteen-year science programme, initiated in 1990, is now half way through and, despite overall government budgetary cuts and reviews, is still on schedule. This has been achieved by a combination of efficiencies in mapping and map production and increased earnings from external sources, which has in turn contributed to a decrease in the cost of core programme overheads.

Around the world, in recent years the budgets and programmes of many surveys have been severely cut, resulting in major staff losses and compromised programmes. The response of the BGS to budget cuts (and I believe it has been the right response for the organization), has been to develop contract and partnership programmes which bring in extra funds and strengthen the BGS's science overall, including the core programme. This has required a careful balance to ensure that the impartiality and scientific credibility of the BGS is not compromised. The nature of this balance was touched on in a recent House of Lords debate on Research in which the Earl of Clancarty said, *"With my emphasis on pure research, I certainly do not wish to deny the use or the results of industry-financed or commissioned research. Rather, there is in a PSRE, such as the British Geological Survey, a fragile and subtle relationship between, on the one hand, the so-called 'core programme' and, on the other, commissioned research — what the BGS calls a 'synergy'. To tamper with one will radically alter the character of the other".*

These and related issues were examined as part of the government's Prior Options Review which enquired whether the BGS and other Public Sector Research Establishments (PSREs) should be privatized. The BGS presented a compelling case for continuing as a not-for-profit public sector organization. The final outcome for the BGS was very satisfactory in that it re-affirmed the need for a national geological survey, accepted that this was best met by the BGS, and concluded that the Survey should remain in the public sector.

Given that the BGS is likely to continue to carry out contract work for the private and public sectors, one of the challenges for the future will be to maintain a balance between the core, partnership and contract programmes and public good and private sector profit, recognizing that in the final analysis that the BGS must put public good first. The complexities of the sort of 'mixed economy' in which the BGS has to work and the issue of public perceptions were highlighted by the recent public enquiry regarding the proposal to establish an underground rock characterization facility (RCF) as part of the investigations by Nirex into options for radioactive waste disposal. The outcome of the enquiry was that the Nirex proposal for an RCF was not accepted. As a result Nirex has stopped most of its programmes. This in turn has had a major impact on the BGS in terms of lost income and termination of radwaste programmes which could make it difficult for the BGS to maintain its position as a leading geoscientific research organization in radwaste. We are applying our radwaste expertize in new areas such as hydrocarbons, but I believe that there is a strong case for public funding of the BGS research in the radwaste area so that we can be in a position to respond to community and industry needs and also provide government with authoritative and impartial advice in an area of great concern to the public at large.

Radwaste is only one of a number of earth science areas where there has been particular government and community interest and concern in recent months. The continuing contraction of Britain's mining industry has been brought into focus by the recent closure of the Asfordby coal mine. The BGS has no role in keeping uneconomic mines working but it does potentially have a major part to play in helping to ensure that planning decisions that affect mineral resources are taken in full knowledge of the geological conditions and that all the relevant resource and environmental information is available to inform the planning process. However, the planning process itself may also need to be modified to fully take all these factors into account.

The issue of geoscience data figured prominently in a recent hearing of the Parliamentary Committee of Science and Technology which commented on the difficulties the BGS has in accessing offshore oil and gas data. The Parliamentary Committee stated *'we believe the current situation (of limiting access to offshore data) is not satisfactory and a higher priority should be given to maintaining the role of the NGIS as the national repository of geological information'.* This is strong support for the BGS position that it should be a one-stop shop for UK geological

data. Great benefit could accrue to industry and the community at large from such an approach, a point put to the Minister for Science, Mr John Battle MP, in discussions earlier this year.

Another area where geology has impacted on politics has been on the island of Montserrat where the BGS has been playing a key role in co-ordinating the work of a large number of scientists involved in monitoring the volcanic activity. Let me acknowledge the outstanding work of the BGS geologists and their colleagues at the Montserrat Volcanological Observatory, work often carried out under hazardous conditions. The BGS work on Montserrat was a topic of particular interest to Her Royal Highness The Princess Royal when she visited the BGS early in 1997 to see something of our international work. The visit also provided us with the opportunity to show Her Royal Highness our activities in providing water supplies to villages in developing countries and also the relationship between geology and human health.

'Geology and the community' is the theme of much of the BGS's work both in Britain and internationally. It was also the focus of a recent (and widely acclaimed) edition of 'Earthwise' in which the Introduction was provided by Mr Allan Rogers, a geologist and a Member of Parliament. The occasion of the 200th anniversary of the birth of Sir Henry De la Beche, the founding Director of the Survey, provided an outstanding occasion during the year for bringing together senior people from industry, government and academia to celebrate a notable occasion and also examine the interface between geology, the community and sustainability.

The past year has served to highlight the relevance of the work of the BGS and of geology in general, to a wide range of environmental issues of importance to industry, the community and government. Rather than being on the margins, the earth sciences are pivotal to finding solutions to some of our most pressing societal concerns including global warming, rising sea levels, natural hazards, pollution and contamination, soil loss and waste disposal, to mention but a few. Earth scientists must be more active in the debate on such issues.

But my final point must be to emphasize the quality and dedication of the BGS staff. Throughout my eight years as Director they have responded extra-ordinarily well to the many changes they have had to face over that time. I am honoured to have been able to lead such an outstanding organization.

Dr Peter J Cook, CBE, DSc, C Geol, FGS,
Director

The BGS is dedicated to provide, on maps and in databases and written accounts, geological information for all parts of Great Britain and her territorial waters, commensurate with the needs of the whole user community.

The CORE PROGRAMME comprises long-term strategic mapping, monitoring, databasing and underpinning applied research. It provides the geoscience knowledge and advice necessary to support informed decision-making by the public and private sectors at the regional and national levels on broad issues relating to resources and the environment. It promotes the public understanding of geoscience issues and is fully funded by Science Budget appropriations.

Geological Mapping of Britain

The 15-year programme of geological mapping carried out within the Multidisciplinary Regional Surveys sub-programme was started in 1990/91. The cumulative outputs over the seven years are 141 resurveyed or revised 1:50 000 geological maps, 51 memoirs and four other books, including three new editions of regional guides. Ten geophysical maps and two sub-surface memoirs have also been produced. During the current year 3559 square kilometres were resurveyed or revised; 247 1:10 000 maps were released to the public (including 30 digital maps), and 102 technical reports were written. Eight shallow boreholes, totalling 595 metres, were drilled. Regional highlights are as follows:

● **East Grampians:** in the Gardenstown area, marine clays were shown to lie within a glaciotectonite unit and to have been emplaced at their present high levels by an ice stream in the Moray Firth. North of

Peterhead, amino-acid dating on shell fragments from the St Fergus silts gave an age between 14 700 and 15 000 years BP. Inland ice retreated early in this area but the 'Scandinavian' ice in the North Sea advanced onto the mainland following deposition of this glaciomarine sequence.

● **Monadhliath:** the complex geology of the Central Highlands is beginning to unravel following the completion of the final area of primary survey left in Scotland. Stratigraphical, structural, metamorphic and isotopic studies have been successfully combined to produce an integrated model of rift basin evolution, orogenesis and magmatism which can now be traced over an area of c. 3000 square kilometres.

● **Lake District:** detailed survey work continues to address the complexity of the Lake District Ordovician volcanoes with mapping now complete over the Keswick district. The volcanic succession is largely younger than that established farther west and contains an exceptionally extensive ignimbrite flow which may prove to be the largest yet recorded in Britain.

● **Southern Uplands:** chemical studies on the distinctive Bail Hill Volcanic Group have proved its alkaline character, ranging from alkali basalt to trachyandesite and with trace-element enrichment patterns typical of oceanic within-plate basalts (*left*). These volcanic rocks are intimately associated with sandstones of the

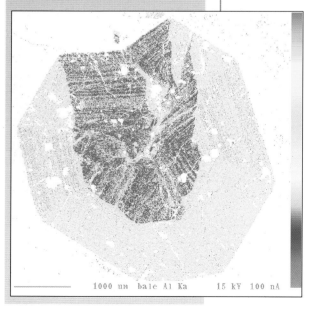

1000 um bale Al Ka   15 kV 100 nA

Single element map of a zoned clinopyroxene phenocryst from Ordovician alkali basalt, Bail Hill, near Sanquhar, Southern Uplands.

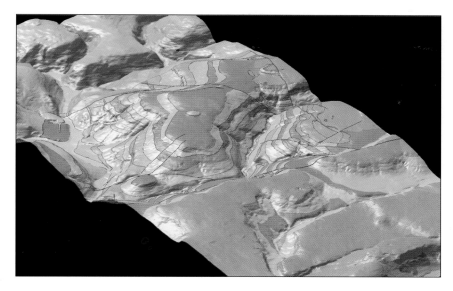

Computer-generated geological relief model of the Huddersfield sheet area looking to the northwest across the Rough Rock escarpment of Highwood Well Moor (foreground, pinkish brown), Luddenden Dean and Crow Hill Nook (centre) and Crimsworth Dean (background) with the Calder valley on the left. Sandstone units (shown in tones of yellow and brown) broadly correspond to topographical ridges: divergence of geological and topographical features indicates the need for review of geological linework.

Kirkcolm Formation, clearly indicating a Caradocian episode of extension and within-plate volcanism in the Southern Uplands terrane.

● **Tyne-Alston:** a review of the Carboniferous rocks of Northumberland, especially in the area between Rothbury and Hexham, has demonstrated the need to redefine the existing stratigraphical classification. This is particularly so in the Namurian part of the sequence, which in Northumberland is dominated by sandstones with evidence of several significant unconformities or non-sequences. The term Morpeth Group has been proposed to encompass this succession, north of the Stublick Fault Zone.

● **Midland Valley:** Lamprophyre-microdiorite sheets in the area north of Stonehaven have calc-alkaline affinities and are shallow level intrusive representatives of the Lower Devonian volcanics of the Midland Valley. Hence they provide a link across the Highland Boundary Fault suggesting that lateral movements were not large.

● For the revision mapping of the **Huddersfield sheet,** trials have been carried out into the effectiveness of the simultaneous interpretation of digital photogrammetry, digital contour models and scanned and digitised primary survey geological lines, to aid the rapid revision of the

geological linework without the need for extensive and costly fieldwork. This technique was compared with the interpretation of computer-generated 3-D geological models produced by combining the existing geological map with the digital contour model (*above*). Both techniques are to be used, the latter for rapid assessment and revision of the existing linework, and the former for the resolution of specific problems identified during that assessment.

● Collaborative work with the University of Sheffield has established a correlation, using spore assemblages, of the Reading Formation in the west of the **London Basin** with the Woolwich Formation in the east. This has implications for the sequence stratigraphical model of the Palaeogene in an interval which currently has poor control.

● Drilling at Swafield, North Walsham, **Norfolk**, penetrated 30 metres of Quaternary sediments which included glacial deposits of the Corton Formation and the underlying Crag, before terminating in Upper Chalk.

● Surveys in **East Devon** and **West Dorset** have revealed extensive areas of deep solution weathering on calcareous Cretaceous rocks. In places, the thickness of the Upper Greensand has been reduced by over 50 per cent and the Chalk has been reduced to a

Detailed Mapping

Detailed mapping of Carboniferous Limestone in two large roadstone quarries near Breedon-on-the-Hill in the East Midlands proved up to about 380 metres of bedded dolostones and massive 'Waulsortian' facies dolostones ranging from early Chadian to Asbian age. An angular unconformity in Cloud Hill Quarry within the sequence has cut out strata of late Chadian to early Holkerian age, and has been proved to be regional in extent.

K Ambrose

Chaotic folding of dolostones and thin interbedded mudstones (dark grey layers) within a slumped sheet of Carboniferous Limestone strata exposed above an unconformity in the north of Cloud Hill Quarry.

Geological Mapping of Britain (continued)

residual rubble containing intact blocks of unweathered material that weigh several thousand tons.

- Extensive and very large scale superficial structures such as cambering and gulling have been recognised during mapping in the **Cotswolds**. Multidisciplinary investigation of the distribution, form and genesis of these structures employs traditional geological mapping and geophysical methods, and newer techniques such as ground penetrating radar and NERC's Airborne Thematic Mapper.

- Mapping in **Dorset, Wiltshire, Hampshire, Sussex** and **Kent,** linked with research at Brighton University, has shown that the Lower, Middle and Upper formations of the important Chalk aquifer of southern Britain can now be subdivided into finer scale mappable members which are readily recognisable by their lithology and topographic expression. The new lithostratigraphy has already been portrayed on three recently published 1:50 000 maps (Wincanton (297), Shaftesbury (313) and Chichester & Bognor (317 & 332)), and will be shown on all future BGS Chalk maps of southern England. The finer detail obtained

improves the understanding of the structure of the Chalk and its relationship to deeper-seated structures of the Variscan basement and concealed Jurassic strata and can be correlated with engineering and hydrogeological parameters.

- In the area around **Plymouth**, mapping and tectonic analysis has enabled the unravelling of the complex sequence of local crustal rifting and extension which accompanied the development of the oceanic basin, the rocks of which now make up the crust of most of western Europe. In addition, continuing work in the **Lizard/Mevagissey** area has refined the understanding of tectonic processes on the 'active margin' of the Rhenohercynian oceanised basin.

Continuous Revision

The purpose of the Continuous Revision programme is to review periodically and keep up to date the 1:10 000 scale geological maps. For example, an effort has been made during the year to produce reconstituted maps for parts of the Sheffield area which were mapped originally prior to extensive opencast coal mining. It also has a policy to target areas in Central Scotland of interest to planners and developers and to present the data as customised themes. Considerable effort has been spent in erecting digital datasets for this purpose. In addition, new data from site investigations, borehole cores and temporary sections have been recorded on 1:10 000 'Correction Copy' maps prior to the production of map updates from the digital map databases.

Small Scale Maps

Preparation of subsurface maps continued using digital methods and included digital databases of key geological surfaces throughout the UK onshore and offshore areas.

*Working for aggregate at Skelbrooke Quarry, near Skellow in dolomitic limestones (Brotherton Formation) of Permian age; reinstatement after landfill is in progress in the middle distance. This locality is within a 1:10 000 sheet recently resurveyed as part of the **West Yorkshire** project.*

J M Hudson

Field Mapping Support

Biostratigraphical determinations contributed in the form of subsurface structural maps and cross sections to the UK onshore mapping programme, integrated with and constrained the results, and assisted in correlation and palaeoenvironmental interpretations on all surface sections and boreholes.

Subsurface Mapping, Cheshire–Staffs Area

Significant advances in the understanding of the subsurface structure and stratigraphy have been made. Seismic data suggest that the margins of the Carboniferous Needwood Basin are bounded by thrust faults.

The North York Moors Holiday Geology Map shows how a satellite image and geological map can be combined for a tourist publication.

Remote Sensing

BGS maintains an ongoing programme aimed at developing practical applications of Earth observation (EO) and remote sensing to help improve the productivity, cost-effectiveness and information content of geological maps and other geoscience products. For the UK, the main emphasis has been on developing techniques of terrain mapping and geomorphological analysis making use of digital photogrammetry based on scanned aerial photographs. Advanced computer systems enable the geologist to view large areas of the ground in full stereo and at high magnification, and to carry out interactive interpretation of featuring, related to bedrock geology, and superficial deposits. The use of draped stereo contours further aid perception and the geologist's comprehension of the landscape. At the same time, techniques have also been implemented on lower-cost computer platforms that enable the geologist to carry out intelli-

gent (i.e. 3-D) on-screen digitisation of geological features directly onto perspectives of the land surface. In effect, the software allows vector lines to be placed onto the surface of the underlying 3-D model. This approach is being used to help evaluate and revise older geological maps by draping the geological linework onto an 'illuminated perspective' of the digital terrain model to see where inconsistencies occur and to correct them. Such approaches help improve accuracy and reduce the amount of fieldwork needed. Similar techniques are also being used to help understand and quantify coastal erosion in the Holderness area (Land-Ocean Interaction Study) and to identify and map landslides in the Bradford area. Geological visualisation is an important tool also in geological understanding and is being used in the new series of BGS popular publications involving the superimposition of satellite images on terrain models *(above)*.

South Staffordshire

Surface mapping and seismic reflection surveys within the Stafford Basin show that Triassic sedimentation within this half graben was controlled by growth on the Brewood Fault — a major basin-bounding structure not previously recognised. In the adjoining Coalbrookdale Coalfield, continued urban regeneration and mineral extraction of opencast coal and brickclay have necessitated revision of maps produced in the 1970s for the Telford New Town.

P A Tod

The importance of the underlying geology to the manufacturing base that developed in the Telford area, South Staffordshire, during the industrial revolution is captured in the tiled 'geological section' which faces one of the retaining walls along the Queensway dual carriageway within the town.

Minerals and Geochemistry of Britain

The BGS carries out systematic geochemical surveying of the UK and maintains national databases of geochemical, radiometric and mineral data.

Support for Mapping

Petrographical work on volcaniclastic samples from the base of the Ordovician Borrowdale Volcanic Group (BVG) in the Lake District revealed a short lived but extensive phase of explosive hydrovolcanism as a precursor to the subaerial lava flow effusion that dominates the lower part of the BVG.

Isotope data derived from rocks of the Lizard Complex and the south Cornwall mélange sequence provided new evidence for a dismembered oceanic basin that now forms part of the Upper Palaeozoic rock sequence of south-west England.

Striking the balance between the need for a sustainable environment and the need for mineral products requires authoritative, systematic information. Technology Foresight has identified the problems and challenges associated with the stages of the natural resource cycle, from exploration, through the identification, extraction, processing and industrial use of resources, to the disposal of waste and the remediation and aftercare of contaminated land. Collectively, the projects that make up the Minerals and Geochemistry Core Programme offer the impartial expertise, knowledge and information on which sound economic and environmental decisions can be based at every stage of the cycle. They also provide fundamental data in support of geological mapping.

G-BASE

The *Geochemical Baseline Survey of the Environment* (G-BASE) provides high resolution baseline geochemical data for soils, stream sediments and waters for economic and environmental applications to international standards. The programme has now completed sampling in the Humber-Trent area, including rural and urban areas.

The geochemical atlas of north-east England was prepared for press, and most of the text for the atlas of north-west England and North Wales *(below)* was written. A hydrogeochemical atlas of Wales (the first of its kind) is in preparation, containing stream water chemistry at a resolution of 1 sample per 2 square kilometres. A thematic section to this atlas illustrates how the data may be used to interpret key issues such as regional controls on trace element mobility, acid rain and eutrophication.

On the international level, the BGS continued to take the lead in initiatives to harmonise geochemical maps and mapping in Europe and worldwide.

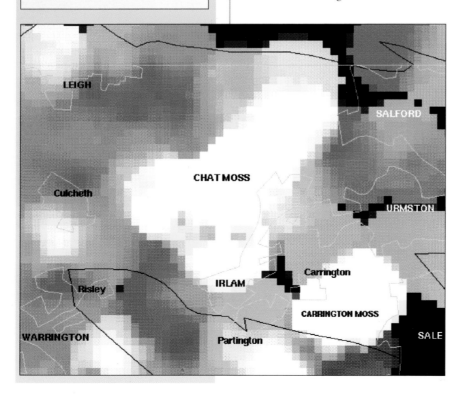

Three-component soil geochemical map (nickel, red; molybdenum green; tin, blue) for the Irlam area, Lancashire, from Regional geochemistry of parts of North-west England and North Wales. *These metals are present at low levels in local bedrock, but values up to 293 ppm, 25.8 ppm and 846 ppm, respectively, are associated with drained fens around Irlam (Chat Moss and Carrington Moss). These mosses were used historically for the disposal of Manchester's street waste, brought down the Ship Canal on barges, distributed over the ground by a light railway system, and then ploughed in. The combination of peaty soil and organic and mineral waste produced a rich, fertile soil which was used for growing vegetables until the 1950s. The association of high heavy metal levels with high calcium, iron and phosphorus values suggests that a large amount of industrial waste such as furnace slag and power station ash was also deposited here.*

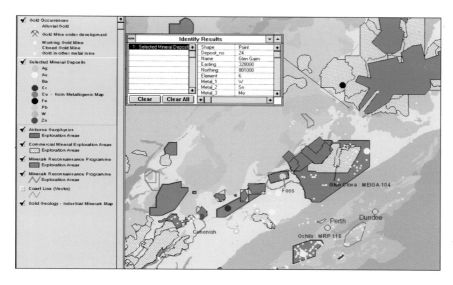

Retrieval from MINGOL for part of Scotland showing detailed airborne geophysical survey areas (blue), Mineral Reconnaissance Programme project areas (red/pink), and selected mineral occurrences (coloured dots) plotted on a monotone geological background.

Minerals GIS (MINGOL)

The prototype MINGOL system, with national coverage of mines and quarries information, is now operational and will be developed further to meet the needs of customers, including DTI and DoE. Digitisation of commercial mineral exploration (MEIGA) project areas is complete, and a prototype mineral exploration GIS, incorporating BGS and commercial mineral exploration data, was demonstrated at the PDAC meeting in Toronto. Information on planning permissions is being incorporated into MINGOL, starting with parts of Cornwall and South Wales. Data are being acquired for the Lake District 1:250 000 sheet, and mineral occurrences, mine and quarry information and planning permissions are being updated. The 1:1.5 million scale gold occurrence map is being developed in cooperation with the Geological Survey of Northern Ireland and the Geological Survey of Ireland. Drafts of five chapters for *Mineral Resources of Britain*, including one on mineral licensing and legislation, have been completed.

Metallogenic Map of Britain and Ireland

This 1:1.5 million scale map was published in collaboration with the Geological Surveys of Northern Ireland and Ireland (GSI), with support from Rio Tinto plc. Symbols indicate the distribution, style and genesis of the principal mineral deposits in Britain and Ireland in relation to their geological setting.

Urban Environmental Survey Multidisciplinary Project

This four year pilot project of the Wolverhampton area has provided a framework methodology for the systematic collection, interpretation and presentation of geoscience data for urban areas using a PC-based GIS system. The data have been used for ranking geohazards to foundation conditions and for evaluating possible public health risks from soil contaminants. A modelling study linking the soil geochemistry data with land use and public health risks has been carried out in collaboration with the Centre for Research into the Built Environment at Nottingham Trent University. In addition, the geochemistry datasets were supplied to the Department of Public Health and Epidemiology in the University of Birmingham, to assist in their population health studies of the West Midlands.

Sedimentary Basin Resources

A pre-publication version of the final report on a multi-discplinary study of the Cheshire Basin, *Basin evolution, fluid movement and mineral resources in a Permo-Triassic setting: the Cheshire Basin*, was made available at a premium price.

Industrial Mineral Resources Map of Britain

This 1:1 million scale map was commended by the British Cartographic Society and awarded the John Bartholomew Award for excellence in small-scale thematic cartography.

NERS

According to the latest NRPB figures, almost three-quarters of the total radiation dose to the average Briton comes from geological sources. The purpose of the *Natural Environmental Radioactivity Survey* (NERS) is to compile baseline data and maps for levels of this natural radioactivity. Radon-potential and gamma-ray exposure maps for the Liverpool Bay area were completed during the year, and work on the Lake District was well advanced.

M H Strutt

Field gamma-ray spectrometer measurements on Ulpha Fell, southern Lake District. The measurements enabled back-calibration of an earlier airborne gamma-ray spectrometer survey.

The data will be used to help compile a gamma-ray exposure map of the Lake District 1: 250 000 sheet for the Natural Environmental Radioactivity Survey.

Geophysics of Britain

UK Magnetic Observatories

New sensors and logging equipment were adopted as the standard systems at the three UK magnetic observatories on 1 January 1997. Automatically generated data products were published electronically on the *Geomagnetism Information and Forecast Service* (GIFS) and accessible via the Geomagnetism Group's World-Wide-Web pages. Near-real-time world-wide observatory data were provided through the *Geomagnetic Information Node for Europe* operated by BGS in the INTERMAGNET programme.

Regional Interpretations

A major new interpretation of crustal structure from geophysical data in North Britain has been completed and will be released shortly as the first publication in the new *Geophysics CD Series*. Publication using HTML on CD has enabled the geophysical data and models to be presented in a variety of formats which show correlations with geological and other information and provide a much greater insight into subsurface structure. The Northern Britain CD includes over 200 colour images, whole-crust 2.5-D gravity/magnetic models along 24 profiles and over 30 3-D models *(below)*.

National Geophysical Surveys and Data Management

Two new gravity maps were prepared in the 1:1000 000 series (Shetland and North Sea). The second (final) phase of the regional gravity survey of the Shetland Isles was completed. Transfer of the land gravity, marine gravity, non-BGS gravity, Wellog and rock stress databases to the new Unix Oracle-based database system was completed and development of new graphical user interfaces commenced. In the case of the land gravity data, the database was completely restructured into relational format.

Interpretation Software

Major new enhancements have been made to the 3-D gravity and magnetic modelling programs (*Gmod and Bmod*) to enable ultra-fast calculation of larger whole-crust models comprising up to 32 layers. The modelling programs now link to a new version of the 3-D viewing program (*GridView*) which has been enhanced to display model layers, sections, observed fields and calculated fields in a variety of viewing options. During the course of the year *Gmod*, *Bmod* and *GridView* have provided a state-of-the-art 3-D modelling capability which has been used to generate gravity models of northern England *(below)* and 'basin thickness' maps of the Rockall-Hatton area for *Geophysical Image Atlas* Volume 11G. Other geophysical software packages were upgraded.

Multicomponent Seismology

Studies of the anisotropic variation of properties of P- and converted waves have improved capability for detection and characterisation of oil-bearing fracture zones in offshore hydrocarbon reservoirs.

Thermal Imaging

Innovative techniques using thermal instrumentation and infra-red photography have been employed in order to detect abandoned mine shafts.

Mapping the geomagnetic field.
Contours of magnetic declination are shown for 1996, when ten (shown in yellow) of the 51 carefully marked repeat stations were reoccupied.

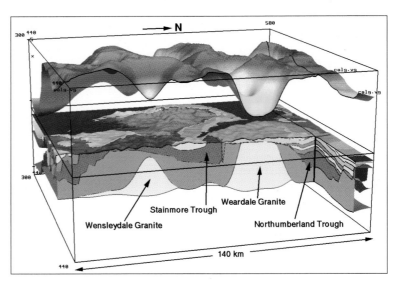

Cut-away of a three-dimensional model of the upper-crustal structure of northern England, based on gravity and seismic reflection data. The colour of the geological units indicates their density, ranging from blue (lowest) to purple (highest). The computed gravitational field is shown in a perspective view above the model. Note the conspicuous gravity minima over the major concealed granites and the way these bodies form the cores of basement highs which are flanked by sedimentary basins.

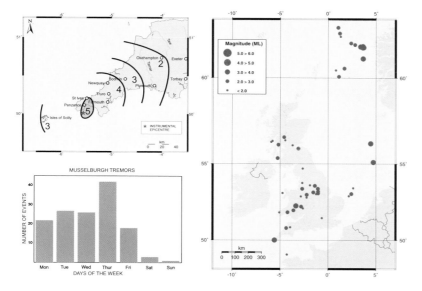

UK seismicity for the reporting period is shown beside a macroseismic survey for the 3.8 ML Penzance earthquake (top left). A swarm of 139 events up to magnitude 2.0 ML caused concern at Musselburgh, east of Edinburgh; additional monitoring instruments were installed. Reduced seismicity at weekends, as shown on the cumulative frequency plot (bottom left), suggests a strong correlation between events and coal mining activity.

Maintenance of Laboratory Capability

Maintenance of the geotechnical and geophysical laboratory capability is crucial to providing a high quality service to industry and in underpinning laboratory and field-based core research. Standard and specialised testing techniques, developed in-house, have been applied to investigations of:

- Swelling and shrinkage of soils.

- Collapse potential of metastable soils.

- Strength and durability properties of building stones.

- Fine-scale structure and petrophysics of reservoir rocks.

- 'Contact' and 'non-contact' microresistivity imaging of whole core.

- Pollution monitoring: a laboratory scale modelling facility.

- Hydraulic properties and magnetic susceptibility logging of rock core.

- Strength of underconsolidated sediments from seismic properties.

- Geotechnical properties of marine sediments.

- Thermal properties of rock samples.

- Pore fluid extraction from clays.

- Physical rock properties for correlation/interpretation of regional geophysical surveys.

Development of Geotechnical Capability

In the developments below, application of geophysical techniques in the laboratory leads to a greater understanding of the control of fine scale sedimentary structure on geotechnical properties; allied field techniques demonstrate geotechnical properties can be inferred from non-invasive subsurface investigations.

- Development of best practice for engineering geophysics used in civil engineering and geotechnical site assessments.

- The use of geophysical methods in the assessment and remediation of contaminated land.

- Subsurface imaging of structure and mass properties using 3-D resistivity tomography.

- Electro-kinetic Seismic (EKS) method to predict the 2-D distribution of subsurface permeability.

- The impact of fine scale geological structure on the assessment of mass properties.

- Development of high resolution core characterisation techniques for the oil industry.

- Characterisation of Quaternary sediments using *Ground Probing Radar*.

The Engineering Behaviour of British Rock and Soil Formations Project

This now includes the investigation of the shrinking and swelling behaviour of clay soils. This property is typically demonstrated by the pronounced polygonal mud cracks shown by high plasticity clays when they shrink as they dry out (*below*).

C D Jones

C D Jones

The sampling of such clays for laboratory determination of their capacity to swell and shrink requires high quality undisturbed samples. To this end a hand sampling device and procedure have been developed in order to cut cylinders (cores) from outcrop and protect them in plastic tubes. This minimises mechanical damage and prevents drying out during transport and storage before testing.

Hydrogeology of Britain

Templars Firs Mud Springs

The occurrence of a group of mud springs, at Temple Firs, Wootten Bassett, were investigated. The linear nature of the springs suggests fault control, with the springs overlying 'chambers' of mud. The mud brings fossils to the surface in an excellent state of preservation and rises from the Amphill Clay, being driven by groundwater rising from the underlying Coral Rag of the Corallian Group. This information has been used to support the aim of designating them an SSSI and development of a protection strategy.

I N Gale

Plumbing the depths of the mud springs at Templars Firs, Wiltshire.

Groundwater Vulnerability

A series of 53 groundwater vulnerability maps, covering the whole of England and Wales at a scale of 1:100 000 are being prepared in association with the Soil Survey and Land Research Centre for publication by the Environment Agency; 40 maps have been published to date. A similar map for part of Scotland is being prepared.

Transport and Fate of Pesticides

This project studies the processes which lead to pesticide contamination in aquifers from diffuse sources and is carried out in collaboration with the Institute of Hydrology, Wallingford. Groundwater movement through the soil and unsaturated zone of the Chalk is determined by use of pressure transducer tensiometers and neutron probes, along with the use of tracer experiments. Field observations of pesticide occurrence in groundwater are made at regular intervals and a novel down-hole sampling device has been developed to sample water freshly arrived at the water table. Laboratory studies have been carried out to obtain degradation rates for specific pesticides in soil and Chalk.

National Groundwater Survey

This project aims to meet identified needs for the comprehensive description of the major British aquifers and their groundwater resources. Studies include the characterisation of the physical and chemical properties and processes which govern groundwater flow and pollutant transport and attenuation, both in the unsaturated and saturated zones.

Attention this year has been focused on the Chalk Aquifer of Yorkshire where co-funded studies of the baseline groundwater chemistry and distribution and movement of nitrate in the aquifer were made. An investigation borehole was drilled at Canaby Moor to help link the stratigraphy to flow horizons as well as provide data for the EC-funded PALAEAUX project *(see page 15).*

Denitrification in the Unsaturated Zone

This was investigated at two research sites, one on the Chalk near Winchester and the other on the Sherwood Sandstone near Mansfield. Overall the results showed no evidence that significant denitrification was occurring in the deep unsaturated zones (below two metres) at either site.

Geosphere Waste Containment: Fluid Flow in Faults and Fractures

Boreholes were drilled in the Mercia Mudstone Group on the Keyworth site for gas injection experiments to study how gases move through mudrocks.

Groundwater Borehole Logging

The Hydrogeology Group logged a record 74 boreholes within the UK. Boreholes have been logged for the Water Industry as well as for stratigraphic and research purposes in a variety of structures ranging from shallow two inches diameter piezometers to 56 inches diameter abstraction boreholes and from 10 to > 500 metres depth. Geophysical logs have also been successfully run down quarry and cliff faces for correlation purposes.

Borehole wireline logging at night, Swanworth Quarry 1.

D K Buckley

Marine and Coastal Geology of Britain

F McTaggart

Trials of the BGS British Mid-Ocean Ridge Initiative (BRIDGE) rockdrill.

Petroleum Geology

- **Palaeogeographic maps and Petroleum Province Map Series.** These maps describing the palaeogeographic evolution and petroleum geology of Lower Cretaceous, and Middle and Upper Jurassic of the Central and Northern North Sea have been prepared. Format and presentational style have been the subject of considerable debate. The maps may be published in Atlas format with marginal material in A3 or A4 format.

- A report on the **uplift patterns on the UK Northwest Atlantic margin** was completed. Future comparative work may provide constraints on paleo-geothermal gradients.

- **Regional seismic interpretation** has provided new insights into the distribution of plume related magmatism in the Rockall Trough and the Northwest Atlantic margin.

- **Petroleum Geology Database:** lithostratigraphic, sequence stratigraphic, seismic and well log data were added to the database.

- **Uplift studies, Northwest Margin:** patterns of uplift on the UK Northwest Margin were analysed by shale interval velocity, vitrinite reflectance measurements and illite crystallinity techniques. Comparison and iteration of the results from these different techniques may provide constraints on paleo-geothermal gradients.

- **Plume-related magmatism, UKCS:** interpretation of new seismic data provided further insights into the geology of the Rockall Trough and the Northwest Margin. The distribution of plume-related magmatism in the Rockall Trough area has been re-evaluated. Interpretations of 3-D seismic surveys were integrated with the regional data set.

Land-Ocean Interaction study (LOIS)

The BGS is the lead Institute for the *Land-Ocean Evolution Perspective Study* (LOEPS) which is a component of the NERC's LOIS project.

Comprehensive support has continued to be provided to LOEPS in respect of core curation and associated scientific services. Framework activities have produced a digital stratigraphic database, an analysis of the anthropogenic contaminant history of parts of the English east coast and have assessed contributions made to marine budgets from coastal erosion through the application of remote sensing techniques.

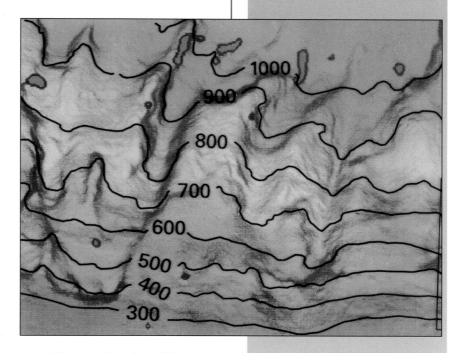

Submarine slope-front failure on the Atlantic margin, northwest of Britain.

The figure illustrates some of the complexity of slides on the slope-front in a region of frontier deep-water oil exploration. Slide-related seabed morphology is enhanced by applying slanted artificial illumination from the east to swath bathymetric data. Bathymetric contours are also illustrated at a contour interval of 100 metres. The sidewall detachment scarps enclosing the main body of the slides typically range from approximately 350 to 1000 metres water depth and appear to have developed into sidewall gullies, illustrated with maximum local shoulder-to-axis depths of approximately 50 metres. The swath bathymetric data were acquired during participation in the LOIS/SES (Land Ocean Interaction Study/Shelf Edge Study) Community Research Programme of the Natural Environment Research Council.

This partnership for technology and knowledge interaction and exchange, contributes to the Government's Technology Foresight programme.

Methane Content of Natural Gases in the UK Permian

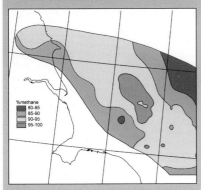

%methane
- 80-85
- 85-90
- 90-95
- 95-100

Percentage of methane in natural gas in UK Permian reservoirs. The composition of natural gas varies significantly between adjacent fields and also vertically within individual fields. The reasons for these variations are not fully understood, and BGS together with four other European Surveys is completing a study of the variability of natural gas in north-west Europe with respect to provenance and depositional environment. A database of gas composition in relation to field, well, source, reservoir, depth etc has been prepared, and contoured data for selected parameters will be presented, accompanied by explanatory text where appropriate. It is expected that the information will be available in hard-copy format and as an interactive CD-ROM.

The PARTNERSHIP PROGRAMME comprises medium-term mapping and research co-funded by the BGS, from Science Budget appropriations, and by partners in the private and public sectors (including the CEC). Such co-funded projects address generic issues relevant both to the Core Programme and to the economic and environmental interests of funding partners. Some examples are shown here.

Working Together

Midland Valley Digital Data

GIS layers of mineral resource data along with associated reports were prepared for customers interested in relating these to non-geological themes.

Natural Attenuation in Polluted Groundwater

This joint EPSRC/EA-funded project between BGS, the University of Bradford and IFE aims to determine the natural rates of attenuation (primarily biodegradation) of organic pollutants in groundwater beneath a coal distillation plant on Triassic sandstones. The field data suggest that redox zonation exists in the pollution plume in the sandstones. The presence of metabolites and actively-dividing bacteria provide support for natural biodegradation reactions in the aquifer.

Computer-aided Decision Making in Mineral Exploration

Co-funding was provided by the DTI for a pilot study linked to BGS metallogenesis and geochemical database work. Potential users amongst minerals-sector exploration and mining SMEs were questioned about their needs and interests, and a prototype demonstration GIS-based system to aid decision-making in metalliferous mineral exploration was developed.

Gas Migration in clays

As a partner in the EC's *'PROGRESS' Project* within in its *Nuclear Fission Safety Programme*, the BGS is examining the impacts of gas migration pathways on the hydraulic properties of clays, along with the capacity for pathway re-sealing after gas flow.

Aquatic Life Charts Environmental Change

In a collaborative study with the University of Bradford, using both the BGS laser ablation microprobe-ICP-MS system and the NERC ion-microprobe facility, changes in the concentration of trace elements in tropical and cold-water corals during growth were observed. It has subsequently been possible to associate these chemical changes with key environmental factors such as temperature and rainfall and to demonstrate the feasibility of using corals for long-term environmental monitoring *(below)*. This type of information has direct application in the assessment of chemical contamination in the vicinity of oil rigs, for example.

T P Cullen

The beautiful coral skeleton of Lophelia Pertusa, *dredged up from the Stanton Banks of Scotland.*

Hydrogeological Classification of Superficial Clays

This project, co-funded by the EA, focuses on the superficial clays in Shropshire and East Anglia. Two 1:50 000 scale clay classification maps have been produced, along with a memoir on the Clay-with-Flints. The project is important for modelling aquifer recharge and for assessing aquifer vulnerability to pollution.

Clay Thermal Analogues

This co-funded EC project aims to investigate natural analogues of the thermo-hydromechanical and thermo-hydro-chemicomineralogical changes which could affect clays used in radioactive waste repositories. The natural analogue information will be used to determine how applicable field data are for studying performance assessment issues relevant to radioactive waste disposal in clay-rich formations or with bentonite backfill.

The Effect of Old Landfills on Groundwater Quality

Site investigations co-funded by the Environment Agency (EA) at the Thriplow landfill site in Cambridgeshire, using the RESCAN geophysical technique and borehole drilling, have confirmed the hydrogeology and shown that the contaminant plume from the landfill lies within ten metres of the water table of the Chalk.

Mining Geophysics

Seismic tomography investigations were undertaken to predict ground instability in conjunction with Laporte Industries and the University of Leeds at Milldam Mine, Derbyshire.

Nearshore Zone Survey

The Inner Thames Estuary 1:50 000 Coastal Geology Series map has been completed. Two sectors of the co-funded *Inshore Seabed Characterisation Project,* Shoreham-Dungeness and Flamborough Head-Gibraltar Point, have been completed. A third sector, the Wash-Winterton, has been completed and awaits approval of the co-funder.

Engineering Geophysics

Off-shore and on-shore cross hole seismic tomography has been undertaken on behalf of the Ministry of defence, UK Nirex Ltd and BNFL in order to determine the geomechanical characteristics of the near-surface, superficial geology. RESCAN imaging has been undertaken in the Sellafield region, Cumbria.

Seismicity Offshore NW UK

Enhancement of the earthquake detection capability for offshore NW Scotland, supported by the Western Frontiers Association, has improved the estimation of seismic risk due to earthquake-triggered landslip on the continental shelf.

Global Geomagnetic Model

The Health and Safety Executive and oil industry consortium-supported 1996 revision of the *BGS Global Geomagnetic Model* (BGGM) and new Windows-style software were produced and distributed, providing magnetic reference data for use in directional drilling of oil and gas wells.

Afon Teifi

This project is cofunded by a consortium of Local Authorities and the Environment Agency. Mapping of the catchment between Lampeter and the coast, together with the drilling of two boreholes has facilitated a fuller understanding of the complex Quaternary deposits that fill much of the Teifi valley. The Quaternary history of the region all appear to relate to the interplay of Irish Sea and Welsh ice sheets and an intervening proglacial lake.

T J Charsley

Tightly folded turbidite sandstones of the late Caradoc Poppit Formation exposed on the foreshore of the Teifi estuary at Poppit Sands, with early Ashgill turbidite mudstones of the Nantmel Formation forming the distance cliffs below Gwbert village. Structures within the sandstones suggest that they were deposited from highly concentrated, fast moving, turbidity currents which flowed from the west or southwest. The rocks were folded during late Caledonian (late Silurian to mid Devonian) earth movements. Surveyed as part of a project partly funded by the local authorities of the Afon Teifi catchment region.

T Harris

Observations being made at the BGS geomagnetic station on Ascension Island, established with oil industry support. Such data contributes to revisions of the BGS Global Geomagnetic Model.

Working Together (continued)

Groundwater Quality in the Yorkshire Chalk

This short study, co-funded by Yorkshire Water, involved characterisation of the baseline quality of groundwater in the Chalk aquifer north of the River Humber, identification of the key processes controlling it and determination of the changes initiated as a result of pollution from agricultural and other sources.

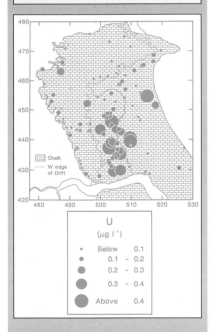

The concentration of uranium in groundwater from the Yorkshire Chalk has a strong redox control: highest values are found in mildly reducing groundwaters from parts of the aquifer

Seismic Risk Evaluation

In partnership with Hiscox Syndicates Ltd, a PC-based seismic risk evaluation program has been developed permitting quick response by insurers to reinsurance requests. Seismic models have been developed for Japan, New Zealand, Turkey, Peru and Chile.

Hydrocarbon Reservoir Imaging

Innovative techniques for processing and interpreting multicomponent and 3-D survey data were adapted for use offshore to match industry requirements. Amplitude Versus Direction (AVD) analysis was successfully tested on Danish chalk gas field data in partnership with Ensign Geophysics as part of an OSO LINK project.

Radioactive Waste

The BGS provided continuous microseismicity monitoring around Sellafield, and also advised on the suitability of multi-component Vertical Seismic Profiles for gathering fracture information.

Joint Studies with British Antarctic Survey

The Lagrelius Point Formation at its type area, northwest James Ross Island, has yielded stratigraphically significant dino-flagellate cysts (including *Herendeenia postprojecta*, *Muderongia* spp. and *Odontochitina* spp.) indicative of an earliest Aptian age.

Stratigraphic Nomenclature, UK Continental Shelf

Standard lithostratigraphic nomenclature schemes, co-funded by consortia of oil companies, have been published for the pre-Tertiary of the North West Margin, and the Carboniferous, Permian and Triassic of the UK offshore East Irish Sea Basin.

Geomechanical Properties of the Rock Mass

This two-year research project, co-funded by the EU, Nirex and four oil companies, has been completed and the final report delivered to the EU. The EU funding was provided under the Joule Programme within a research consortium comprising seven European universities and two other institutes. The project was concerned with characterisation of discontinuities (joints, faults and veins) in the bulk rock mass and understanding their interaction at a local scale with the regional stress field *(below)*.

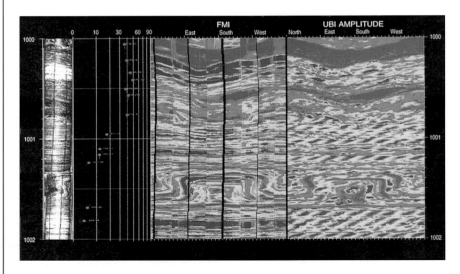

Wellog display of a two metres section of borehole wall image and rock core photograph exhibiting a prominent kink fold

Seismic Interpretation, UK Continental Shelf

Interpretation of new surveys on the UKCS has provided services to the oil industry, and new evidence of Paleogene inversion tectonics on the Mid North Sea High.

Magnetic Properties of Sedimentary Rocks

A major project to characterise the magnetic properties of sedimentary rocks in UK basins has been completed and the results delivered to the (six) oil companies which provided co-funding.

FieldBank

Project *FieldBank* (gravity and magnetic data management) is co-funded by OSO and is being carried out in collaboration with ARK Geophysics and Petroleum Exploration Computer Consultants. It aims to establish a POSC-compliant data model for gravity and magnetic data and implement an 'industry standard' data management system using PECC's Petrovision software.

Europrobe

BGS continued the scientific leadership of the *Trans-European Suture Zone* (TESZ) project of the EUROPROBE programme which brings together multi-disciplinary, multi-national teams to study the structure and tectonic evolution of the European lithosphere. EU funding was secured for a new network (URO) to co-ordinate research on the Uralides project.

National Groundwater Survey — Tracer Studies

As part of a three year Environment Agency/BGS funded study, radial flow tracer tests have been performed in both the Chalk and the Sherwood Sandstone. The tests were performed primarily to develop a protocol for tracer testing which will help practitioners design successful tests.

UK Groundwater Forum

This was formed to promote a co-ordinated approach to groundwater research. Activities in 1996/97 included seminars on landfill leachate migration and aquifer storage and recovery and the production of a book introducing groundwater to the layman. The Forum is also compiling a database of current groundwater research in the UK that should facilitate communications between members of the research community and sponsoring organisations. Access to this database is through the Forum's Internet home page at: http://www.nwl.ac.uk/gwf/

Groundwater in Urban Development

An advanced draft of an initial Volume *Assessing Management Needs and Formulating Policy Strategies* which comprises the first part of an urban policy paper commissioned by ODA for World Bank use, has been completed and internally reviewed by World Bank officials.

Kamchatka

Funded by INTAS (EC)/SB the objectives of the study are the scientific investigation and protection of unique hydrothermal phenomena and to build an up-to-date portfolio of the landscape characteristics of the Kamchatka Peninsula and to relate these to issues relevant to the effective management of this unique ecosystem *(see right)*.

Recharge of Grand Erg

The objectives of this study, which have been part funded by the EC Avicenne Initiative, have been to investigate the limits of sustainable development in the aquifer of the Grand Erg Orientale underlying the areas of eastern Algeria and southern Tunisia.

Palaeaux

Aquifers in coastal Europe are under severe pressure due to human settlement, industry and tourism. In addition they are threatened by climate change and likely sea level rise. The Palaeaux Project supported by the EC Framework IV Environment and Climate Programme and involving partners from nine European countries, seeks to investigate the effects on these aquifers of the drastic fluctuations in climate experienced in the late Pleistocene and Holocene (last 50 000 years).

Baseline Geochemistry — UK Groundwaters

Funded by the Environment Agency, this project aims to produce a synthesis of regional groundwater quality information from selected aquifers in England and Wales in order to characterise the baseline chemistry of groundwaters as a benchmark to present and future pollution risk.

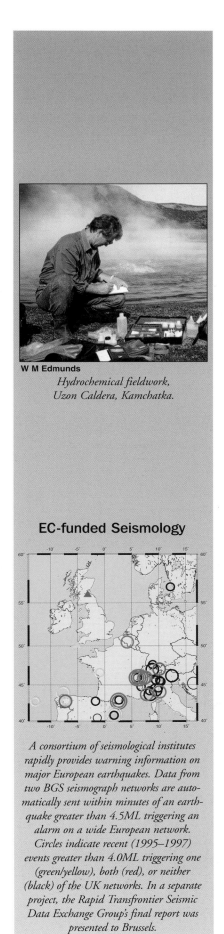

W M Edmunds

Hydrochemical fieldwork, Uzon Caldera, Kamchatka.

EC-funded Seismology

A consortium of seismological institutes rapidly provides warning information on major European earthquakes. Data from two BGS seismograph networks are automatically sent within minutes of an earthquake greater than 4.5ML triggering an alarm on a wide European network. Circles indicate recent (1995–1997) events greater than 4.0ML triggering one (green/yellow), both (red), or neither (black) of the UK networks. In a separate project, the Rapid Transfrontier Seismic Data Exchange Group's final report was presented to Brussels.

The synergy between UK-based work and overseas operations, as well as vice versa, is one of the BGS's greatest strengths.

The **CONTRACT PROGRAMME** comprises medium- and short-term research undertaken in direct response to commissions from customers in both the public and private sectors and fully funded by them. Projects build upon the expertise developed within the Core Programme and return knowledge and skills to it.

Geology Worldwide

Colombia

Collaboration and discussions are continuing with Colombia to assist with the restructuring of the Colombian coal ming industry. Rock mechanics and engineering geology play an important role in predicting the likelihood and magnitude of mining subsidence, landslides, and underground mine failure in a region where earthquakes and volcanic activity complicate the ground deformation mechanisms. The application of rock mechanics and engineering geology to petroleum exploration is an area of potential collaboration between the Colombian petroleum industry and BGS. In addition, ground subsidence due to oil extraction requires the application of mining ground deformation knowledge.

L J Donnelly

Mining induced structural damage due to the Amaga Angelopolis coalfield.

Northern Ireland

The Geological Survey of Northern Ireland (GSNI) is led by BGS scientists. It is an office of the Department of Economic Development and advises on all geological matters, especially contributing to the licensing administration for minerals and petroleum.

A new 1:250 000 scale geological map covering all the solid rocks of the north of Ireland was completed and will form the basis for future exploration for minerals and hydrocarbons. Detailed survey of the Dalradian (Precambrian) rocks of the Dungiven district, a gold target area, continued. Remote sensing and other rapid survey techniques were applied to producing a map of the Ballymena district which was completed within the year. The district is significant in particular for reasons of water supply from superficial deposits and planning concerns relating to major ancient landslips, some periodically reactivated, along the edge of the Antrim Plateau.

Earth Science Conservation Review work for the Department of the Environment (NI) was completed for all the Upper Palaeozoic and Mesozoic rocks of Northern Ireland. Work on the Precambrian rocks satisfactorily reached the mid-point of the contract.

The first Directory of Geosciences in Ireland, prepared in collaboration with the Geological Survey of Ireland (GSI), was published in Dublin. Another co-operative GSNI/GSI project produced tourist guides to the landscape and rocks of counties Cavan and Fermanagh. This has led to a successful application for European funding to develop tourism products and markets across the twelve counties of Northern Ireland.

Additionally, a project to establish common cross-border standards for mineral maps has won funding. The aim in both projects is to help boost local economies, especially in rural districts with high unemployment.

A database of abandoned mines in Northern Ireland was completed, including some 2000 shafts mostly left by mining for coal, bauxite, iron ore, lead and salt. Monitoring of abandoned salt mines in south Antrim continued, with mines that have had support pillars removed by the past process of brining continuing to give concern.

Several technical reports were produced during the year, including the first Inventory of Quarries, Pits and Mines, and a study of metallogenesis in the Precambrian rocks of the Sperrin Mountains.

Angola

A project entitled *Economic Management Capacity Building Project, Institute Support Component* is being implemented with World Bank funding in conjunction with the Angolan Ministry of Geology & Mines. The project aims to strengthen the information base on the country's mineral resources and improve its dissemination to the industry.

Bolivia

The BGS is working with the National Geological and Mineral Service of Bolivia (SERGEOMIN) in the design and installation of a geological and minerals database, supported by the World Bank. Visits have been made to offices not only in La Paz but also Oruro and Santa Cruz de la Sierra.

Botswana

In Botswana one Principal Regional Geologist (funded by the ODA) was at

The Red Sea is red in this colour-ratio-composite (band 5/7=red, 5/1=green, 4=blue) Landsat Thematic Mapper satellite image of western Sinai, Egypt, (80 km east-west) taken on 29 July 1990 from an altitude of 705 km This choice of band ratios allows the discrimation of some of the rock types with high TM7 absorptions such as clays (mudstones, kaolinitic sandstones, altered granites, altered dolerite dykes), sulphates (gypsum, anhydrite) and carbonates (limestones and dolomites); while the very-near-infrared band 4 preserves topographic information, which is useful for mapping geologic structures and lithology. The Red Sea in this image owes its colour to the low reflectance of water molecules at TM7 wavelengths, thus increasing its 5/7 ratio.

post in the Botswana Geological Survey Department during the year. He is Adviser to the Director with particular responsibilities for the national geological mapping programme and associated training. Mineral prospection is at record levels in Botswana and advice was also given to the exploration companies. The BGS Geologist has compiled a new 1:1 million national geological map that is scheduled to be printed in 1998 (the 50th anniversary of the Botswana Geological Survey Department). The geologist's departure later in 1997 will close 31 years of continuous, post independence, residential support by the BGS.

Ecuador

The Geological Information Mapping Programme active since 1995 has had five residential BGS staff in Quito concerned with geological and geochemical mapping of the Western Cordillera. The ODA-funded project is to be widened to the field of metallogenetic investigation for the *Assessment of Ore Districts* under World Bank funds. Two BGS economic geologists will be assigned to this new two year programme. BGS residential teams have been in Ecuador for a total of twenty years and have visited every corner of the country.

Falkland Islands

A BGS geologist resident in Stanley since early 1996 is undertaking a geological map of the onshore area of the Falkland Islands at a scale of 1:250 000 together with a report describing the geology of the islands. This work is being undertaken with the cooperation of the first Falkland Islands geology graduate.

Guyana

The Commonwealth Fund for Technical Cooperation is supporting the Guyana Geology and Mines Commission by funding the BGS for two years to advise on the creation of a modern database for minerals information and mining records as well as training in a variety of geoscience topics.

Hong Kong

Three BGS staff remained on secondment to Hong Kong under contract to the Geotechnical Engineering Office (GEO) throughout the year. The marine geologist returned to the BGS in early 1997 but the Head of the Hong Kong Geological Survey, and one other BGS geologist have signed contracts to stay in Hong Kong for a further three years under the new administration.

Jordan

An institutional twinning relationship exists between the Natural Resources Authority (NRA) of Jordan and the BGS. This product of a long standing relationship starting in 1984 has maintained the 1:50 000 geological mapping and map and bulletin production, and in 1997, in a new phase of ODA support, saw the commencement of a training programme in environmental thematic mapping and hazard assessment to be accompanied by advice on the design of an engineering geology database.

Assistance was also given to the Water Authority of Jordan (WAJ) on the assessment of natural radionuclides in groundwater used for domestic purposes.

Egypt

The BGS played a prominent role in the centenary celebrations of the Egyptian Geological and Mining Authority (EGSMA) held in Cairo in November 1996. As well as a number of presentations on collaborative studies in the Eastern Desert, BGS also contributed a 1:1 000 000 geological map of the Precambrian rocks of the Eastern Desert together with an explanatory text.

Entitled *One Hundred Years of Geological Partnership British-Egyptian Geoscientific Collaboration,* the publication *(below)* details the origin and growth of the EGSMA and the British geologists in this process. Over the past 17 years the ODA has funded collaboration between the BGS and EGSMA with geological mapping, mineral exploration and associated training being the focus of the relationship.

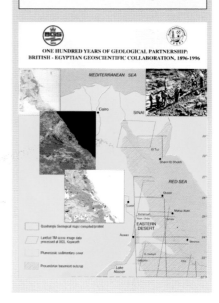

Geology Worldwide (continued)

Papua New Guinea

The petroleum exploration and development technical assistance project for the Government of Papua New Guinea, funded by the World Bank began in October 1995 and will run until the end of 1999. BGS has provided a multidisciplinary residential team of two petroleum geoscientists, legal and fiscal experts, and pipeline, drilling and production engineers. The team is supported by short-term expertise in information technology and related disciplines to complement the residential inputs. A computer network was designed and installed. Team members provided advice and material input into such matters as selection of the PNG Refinery Bid; privatisation of the government share of oil and gas field equity; landowner issues; and drafting of oil and gas legislation and model agreements.

Sri Lanka

A World Bank-funded contract with the Sri Lankan Government for the BGS to work with the Geological Survey and Mines Bureau was completed during the year. Seven full colour 1:100 000 scale geological maps were completed, which

altogether amounts to just under 50 per cent of the land area of Sri Lanka.

Syria

The (BGS) has been working in collaboration with the General Establishment for Geology and Mineral Resources (GEGMR) at the Ministry of Petroleum and Mineral Resources in the field of environmental geology.

The collaboration, funded by the British Embassy, Damascus through the British Partnership Scheme, focused on training geoscientists in the methodology and techniques of applied geological mapping by means of short courses and practical studies in Damascus and the Mediterranean coastal region. The aim was to assist the GEGMR in developing their environmental geology maps and supporting databases using GIS and computer databases.

Practical studies were carried out on key issues in the coastal region, including: landslides, natural cavities in limestone, groundwater quality, abstraction of beach sand and coastal erosion, siting and control of landfill, monitoring of radon gas, and sustainable development of industrial mineral resources. A trial GIS was developed for the Safita geological sheet, and it is hoped that the successful collaboration will be extended to other areas of the country.

Trinidad

Collaboration and discussions are continuing with Trinidad in the field of engineering geology and rock mechanics and the failure of volcanic domes.

Zambia

In cooperation with the Geological Survey Department of Zambia, a two year project is being undertaken with EU funding to edit, produce and publish, geological maps and associated reports. This project, which has a strong training emphasis, reinforces earlier map production work funded by the World Bank.

Basaltic Tephras

Geochemical analysis of tephra layers were studied in relation to a two-year ROPA award. It provides a record of Plinian pyroclastic eruptions that deposited ash in an easterly to southerly direction from the North Atlantic Tertiary Igneous Province (NATIP).

Syria: siting an aggregate quarry NE of Safita.

J H Powell

Falkland Islands Petroleum Consultancy

Enhanced imagery: NERC & Falkland Islands Government

The Falkland Islands Government utilised the BGS for support in developing offshore exploration in assessing bids for licences during the first Licensing Round. Drilling operations are planned to start early in 1998, following the interpretation of new 2-D and 3-D seismic data. BGS is also working with the Falkland Islands Government to develop a further licencing round southwest of the islands in collaboration with the UK and Argentine governments through the South West Atlantic Hydrocarbon Commission.

HYDROCARBONS

Sequence stratigraphy: the BGS have developed and run a field course in Utah, USA, examining the sequence stratigraphy of classic outcrops, and the limitations and advantages of applying sequence stratigraphic models to exploration and production, with particular reference to North Sea reservoir analogues.

DTI Hydrocarbons contract: five geoscientists, based at the Department of Trade and Industry office in Edinburgh, continue to provide the Oil and Gas Division of the DTI with advice on various aspects of exploration, appraisal and development in the UK.

Stratigraphic nomenclature: the standard nomenclature scheme for the Pre-Tertiary sedimentary succession west of Shetland was published in A3 atlas format. A similar volume describing the lithostratigraphy and sequence stratigraphy of the Paleogene is in press. An A3 volume describing a standard nomenclature scheme for the Carboniferous, Permian and Triassic of the UK offshore East Irish Sea Basin was published.

Commercial collaboration: seismic interpretation reports were prepared for Geoteam AS, based on their new regional surveys covering the Mid North Sea

High, the northern White Zone and the western flank of the Rockall Trough.
Small-scale maps: summarising information on depth to the Moho, and the character of basement terranes across the UK Northwest Atlantic margin, were prepared for an international oil company.

Focused biostratigraphical support was given to hydrocarbon industries in the Gulf Region, Algeria, Ecuador, Germany, The Netherlands and UK Continental Shelf. Heavy minerals studies assisted Reservoir Provenance studies, and were used in monitoring horizontal drilling.

Training courses in *Extensional Tectonics, Seismic Interpretation,* and *Sequence Stratigraphy* were given.

Technical assistance, Papua New Guinea: a BGS team of nine petroleum specialists provided training and advice on exploration and appraisal to the Government of Papua New Guinea. Training has included seismic interpretation and hydrocarbon prospectivity assessment of the North New Guinea Basin.

An international petroleum geology study was initiated on behalf of a major oil company.

P C Richards

In the Paradox Basin, Utah, the Moab Fault at Bartlett Canyon juxtaposes Entrada Formation (Jurassic) in the footwall against Cedar Mesa Formation (Cretaceous) in the hanging wall (see Sequence stratigraphy).

Geology Worldwide (continued)

Papua New Guinea

In Papua New Guinea the development of the Lagifu/Hedina oilfield during the last ten years has led to the construction of support infrastructure for the extraction and transport of oil. A concern that associated bridge construction was affecting the flow of the Mubi river *(below)* prompted a consultancy by the BGS to investigate the problem. These studies concluded that the engineering work had no permanent effect on the river behaviour. Further studies downstream into the effects of pipeline construction on sedimentation in the river were also conducted.

View downstream of the sediment-charged and turbid Waga River, with the clear Mubi River on the right.

Rapid Global Geological Events

This NERC special topic requires continuous rock cores through the full thickness of the Jurassic Kimmeridge Clay together with a full suite of downhole geophysical logs. The BGS was awarded the contract to obtain these data, and to provide the preliminary stratigraphical interpretation and correlation with the Dorset type section that will provide the framework for the university sampling programmes. Excellent core recovery was achieved; taken together, the cores from three boreholes drilled near to the type section of the Kimmeridge Clay provide the best record of the formation recorded to date.

FUGAP

A Forum for Urban Geology and Planning in SE Asia and the Pacific (FUGAP) has been set up by ESCAP, based in Bangkok, to promote the use of earth science in planning and development. The BGS has attended meetings held in Bangkok and Shanghai, providing advice on the presentation of earth science information, the establishment of databases and the use of GIS.

Newham Borough, London

Using GIS techniques developed under the Wolverhampton urban study *(page 7),* the BGS is investigating the London Borough of Newham. An evaluation of susceptibility to natural methane gas hazards has been completed and work is continuing on aspects of land use and soil geochemistry.

Human Risk in Relation to Landfill Leachate Quality

The main objective of this ODA-funded project is to produce a catalogue of leachate quality, and assess the risk to human health associated with the uncontrolled release of landfill leachates. Groundwater sampling programmes in Mexico, Thailand and Jordan, in collaboration with local counterparts, are directed at studying temporal variation in groundwater and leachate quality in response to seasonal changes.

Bradford

The findings of a study into the relevance of earth science issues in the City of Bradford Metropolitan District, funded by the Department of the Environment, were released at a presentation at Bradford City Hall, attended by members of the Local Authority and local developers, engineering geological consultants and conservation groups.

Remote Sensing Overseas

Satellite remote sensing forms an important part of many overseas projects, particularly where large areas of country need to be covered quickly and accurately at reconnaissance scale. Imagery from space provides a synoptic view from which information can be obtained on the distribution of rock types, structures and mineralisation, indications of groundwater, or the effects of natural hazards such as earthquakes, volcanic eruptions and landslides. Recent inputs have been provided to geological projects in Ecuador, Falkland Islands, Hong Kong, Egypt and others.

J W C James

Seabeds and Coasts around the World

Land Ocean Contamination Study (LOCS)

This ODA-funded project focused on three contrasting urbanised coastal settings: the East African ports of Mombasa and Dar es Salaam; Jakarta Bay; and Sepetiba Bay, Brazil. In each area geochemical, ecotoxicological and oceanographic surveys were undertaken in order to improve the regional capacity for identifying and mitigating coastal pollution hazards. A workshop was held in Mombasa to disseminate the results and implications of LOCS case-studies in East Africa to scientists and policy-makers.

Seabed Mobility Study

Work has started with HR Wallingford and the University of Southampton on a contract for CIRIA investigating the regime of seabed sediment transport in an area to the west of the Isle of Wight. The study aims to provide the scientific basis for assessing the impacts of proposed aggregate dredging, notably on the stability of the adjacent shorelines.

Shoreline Management

A report was completed through Halcrow for the North Devon and Somerset Group of Coastal Authorities on the geology and sediment transport processes relating to the Shoreline Management Plan for this area of the Bristol Channel.

Hong Kong Airport

A detailed study was completed of five onshore cored boreholes at the new airport site at Chek Lap Kok, to serve as stratigraphic reference sections for the geotechnical database of the airport platform. The work concludes a major study of the platform geology by the BGS, serving the requirements of the geotechnical design for the airport construction. The key to understanding the marine geology of Chek Lap Kok airport is the integration of seismic borehole and CPT data to produce a comprehensive 3-D geological framework.

Irish Sea Geochemical Database

A report prepared jointly with MAFF Burnham Laboratory on a scoping study for the production of a database of sediment geochemistry for the Irish Sea has been submitted to the Department of the Environment.

Cable Route Surveys

Reports were completed for National Grid plc on the assessments of seabed and associated landfall conditions for cable installation between Douglas, Isle of Man, and Cumbria and Anglesey respectively. Another report completed for BT Marine assessed seabed conditions in part of the North Sea.

Ground Level Change, Thames Estuary

The initial phase of a study which will use differential GPS to monitor long-term ground level changes that could increase the susceptibility of the Thames Estuary region to marine flooding has been carried out jointly with IESSG, University of Nottingham.

Coastal Erosion in Zanzibar

A study for the Commission for Lands and Environment in Zanzibar and funded by the Royal Netherlands Government reported on the threat to the islands' vulnerable shorelines through coastal erosion.

R S Arthurton

A coastal dweller cycles home along a Zanzibar beach on a platform-fringed coast.

Worldwide Minerals and Geochemistry

The BGS provides capabilities in the fields of geochemical surveying, environmental geochemistry, the assessment of industrial and metalliferous mineral resources, mineral intelligence and statistics, and specialist laboratory services.

ODA Mining Advisor

The advisor led a BGS team to Angola on a project to support the Ministry of Geology and Mines. Advice was provided in institutional strengthening and in the establishment of a minerals deposit database. The role of the Mining Adviser is to support the ODA/Foreign Office in the mounting of projects under the Know How Fund which helps the countries of eastern Europe to improve their commercial practices. The Mining Adviser also provides services in the assessment of multilateral aid projects.

Mineral Resource Information for Development Plans

A methodology was developed for the DoE for the collection and display of data on the distribution of mineral resources and their relationship to national planning designations. The purpose of the work is to assist in the preparation of development plans in relation to minerals extraction and the protection of mineral resources against sterilisation. Digital mineral resource and constraint maps on the scale of 1:100 000 with accompanying interpretative reports are being prepared for twenty mineral planning authorities in England and Wales.

Computer-based 3-D Modelling

Using VULCAN software, the computer-generated structural and mining development model of the Foss orebody was extended in liaison with the company's geologists. The system was also used in contracts from SMEs in the mineral exploration and development sector, including the modelling of extensive gold-bearing alluvial deposits in the FSU and fault-disrupted stratabound deposits, and contributed to work for NIREX, including the 3-D modelling of salinity in groundwater and development of the site model.

Minerals Programme, UK

This programme, funded by the DTI, combines the work of the *Mineral Intelligence Programme* and parts of the *Mineral*

Reconnaissance Programme (MRP), whose activities were drastically reduced and re-oriented. The new programme comprises two sections: a minerals information and advisory service and activities aimed at promoting and creating wealth from Britain's mineral resources.

Five MRP reports containing evidence of new mineralisation were issued during the year. An assessment of the potential for gold mineralisation in the Southern Uplands of Scotland, using integrated digital geological, geophysical, geochemical and mineral occurrence datasets and paying particular attention to structural controls, identified 22 target areas; test sampling in some of these areas confirmed the presence of gold, validating the computer-based target selection criteria and indicating that follow-up work was merited.

In the Scottish Highlands, several localities were identified in the Dalradian which had potential for industrial-grade garnet. Exploration in the Glenelg area indicated that the Strathconan fault system was a favourable target for vein-style gold mineralisation and that graphitic gneisses with a carbon content reaching 16 per cent have potential as a source of crystalline graphite. Indications of gold enrichment in the Dalradian of Knapdale *(see left)* are associated with base-metal bearing quartz veins; analysis of geophysical and remotely-sensed lineations indicated the importance of structural controls on the distribution of gold.

Gold was identified in alluvial sediment derived from Permian red beds and alkali basalts in the Mauchline and Thornhill basins of Southern Scotland and at localities in central and south-west England. The findings supported the mineralisation model developed for Permo-Triassic red beds in Devon.

The information and advisory service provided information to government and industry on all aspects of minerals exploration, development, production and trade, making extensive use of databases

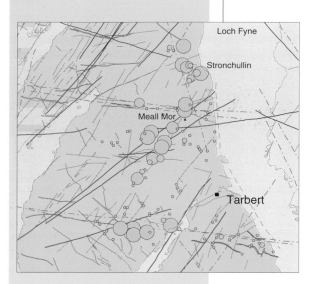

Distribution of gold in panned concentrates (yellow) in relation to regional gravity lineations (blue), aeromagnetic lineations (dash-dot red), quartz-dolerite dykes (green) and mapped faults and Tertiary dykes (magenta) in south Knapdale.

supported by the programme. Work included participation in the *International Strategic Metals Issues* (ISMI) Working Group and in an International Consultative Group in Non-ferrous Metal Statistics. The *World Mineral Statistics* database which contains information on the production and trade of minerals world-wide, compiled from official sources and in consultation with major producers, traders and other international organisations, was updated and *World Mineral Statistics 1991–95* produced from it. This annual publication was upgraded by the incorporation of world maps illustrating the production of 12 commodities and graphical illustration of world production through time of 22 commodities. Also published was *United Kingdom Minerals Yearbook 1996,* providing detailed statistics for the UK and including commentary and graphics.

Human Selenium Imbalances

ODA-funded investigations of the environmental geochemical controls of selenium-responsive diseases continued in collaboration with Chinese and Sri Lankan geochemists and medical scientists. An investigation was carried out to evaluate the relationship between environmental selenium concentrations and oesophageal cancer incidence in the Cixian area, China. Selenium is important in thyroid hormone metabolism, and hypothyroidism is intensified when both iodine and selenium are deficient. At least one billion people are at risk from iodine deficiency disorders (IDD) including goitre, cretinism and mental retardation. An investigation was initiated in Sri Lanka of the relationship between selenium deficiency and iodine deficiency disorders.

Mercury Pollution Hazards

Work continued in collaboration with government departments in the Philippines and Ecuador on this ODA-funded project to develop techniques for monitoring the magnitude and impact of mining-derived mercury pollution in tropical developing countries. A detailed assessment of human mercury exposure in an artisanal mining area on the Philippine island of Mindanao was completed, and preliminary hydrochemical surveys were undertaken in the Nambija and Ponce Enriquez gold mining fields of Ecuador.

Namibia

A programme of technical assistance and institutional strengthening is being undertaken in Namibia by two BGS geologists who have undertaken a two-year project to set up an industrial minerals laboratory, prepare a national inventory of industrial minerals and organise a modern database. The project is supported by EU SYSMIN funding.

Surinam

A technical assistance contract funded by the European Community has been awarded to BGS to undertake a study preparatory to the establishment of a minerals institute in Paramaribo.

Geoscience Information Systems for Mineral Development

Visits to Malaysia, Guyana and Botswana in connection with this ODA-funded project showed that, despite local variations, there are many similarities in the mineral rights legislation. These findings have enabled a full logical database design to be completed.

Northern Ireland

Geochemical sampling over the western part of Northern Ireland was completed during the year. Early results showed the presence of high fluoride values over Carboniferous rocks in the south of the area, and further observations of gold in panned concentrates over Dalradian rocks in the north-east.

Laboratory Services

Over 25 000 samples were analysed in the BGS analytical geochemistry laboratories during the year, in support of BGS projects and an increasing number of external commercial clients. Method development has continued, of particular note being the rapid determination of halogens in crystalline rocks and clays.

The Sample Preparation Facility has developed new methods designed to prepare small or malleable materials for chemical analysis and physical testing, such as teeth, bone, muscle fibres, bitumen-bound aggregates and plastics.

The Thin Sectioning Service continued to develop a world-wide network of customers through the BGS Professional Services web page.

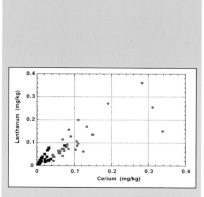

Endomyocardial Fibrosis (EMF) *is a fatal form of heart disease which affects children and young adults across the tropics. The BGS is working with the Centre for International Child Health (Great Ormond Street, London) and Mulago Hospital (Kampala, Uganda) with ODA funding to examine links between the occurrence of this disease in Uganda, magnesium deficiency and exposure to cerium. Research with the Eastman Dental Institute has demonstrated that cerium levels in deciduous teeth from Uganda* (in red) *are clearly above those observed in a similar subsample of children from the United Kingdom* (in blue).

S D J Inglethorpe
Geologists from the Thai Department of Mineral Resources (DMR) and BGS logging the upper part of a diatomite quarry section, as part of a project led by the Camborne School of Mines and funded by ODA to compile an inventory of the diatomite deposits of Changwat Lampang, northern Thailand, for use in the treatment of contaminated land.

Worldwide Geophysics and Geohazards

Montserrat

As part of the British Government concern for the safety of the islanders of the British Dependent territory the BGS is closely monitoring the seismic and volcanic activity of the volcano through the Montserrat Volcanic Observatory and has participated in the formulation of emergency planning with the British Governor and local authorities. The broad band radio-linked seismometer network installed around the Soufrière Hills volcano continues to detect hundreds of events daily. Detailed seismicity reports were provided to engineering companies requesting site-specific hazard information over other areas of the world.

L J Donnelly

13 May 1996: Tar River pyroclastic flow reaches the Atlantic Ocean from the Montserrat volcano.

Seismic Properties of Sea-floor Rocks and Sediments

Knowledge of the acoustic and geotechnical properties of the sediments and underlying bedrock layer is required for input into the Defence Research Agency's model for the propagation of sound through them. A consolidation cell has been developed into which geophysical transducers and additional fluid outlets have been incorporated, enabling permeability, porosity and associated seismic wave properties to be measured on sediments under effective pressures up to two MPa.

Geophysical Imaging of Gas Migration

This is part of an Engineering and Physical Sciences Research Council-run project involving the injection of gas through a clay sample, and the mapping of the gas migration. The aim of the project is to provide the capability for resistivity monitoring of clay samples as gas is injected through them. The object is to carry out a full suite of tests, in the resistivity cell, using the CORSCAN Logging apparatus and the gas injection apparatus simultaneously.

Monitoring Changes in Regional Ground-level

Funded by the Environment Agency, a project is being carried out with the Institute of Engineering Surveying and Space Geodesy to establish a network of 25 GPS receivers in the London Basin, sited in order to test one or more potential mechanisms of ground movement. These include shrinkage of Holocene sediments, swell-shrink of London Clay, valley bulge and aquifer recharge and depletion.

Geophysical Image Atlases

The Geophysical Image Atlas continued to attract strong commercial interest in the hydrocarbons sector. Three new volumes were produced to provide gravity and magnetic information to companies working on the Atlantic margin and northern North Sea. New volumes 11G and 11M (Hatton Bank) complete the Atlas coverage of the UK Atlantic margin (together with volumes 9G&M (Shetland-Faeroes) and 10G&M (Hebrides-Rockall) produced last year). New volume 7G provided improved regional gravity coverage of the northern North Sea based on a new compilation of BGS and non-BGS data.

Integrated Modelling

Integrated 2-D and 3-D seismic-gravity-magnetic modelling was carried out for several oil companies working on the Atlantic margin to assist their understanding of sub-basalt structure. 3-D modelling was carried out using the new, ultra-fast, BGS 3-D gravity modelling program *Gmod*.

Northern Ireland

A major study has been completed for the Department of Economic Development to provide information for the hydrocarbons and minerals industries in order to stimulate exploration in Northern Ireland. The regional gravity and aeromagnetic data have been re-interpreted using 2-D and 3-D modelling techniques and the results presented in the form of an interpretation report and *Geophysical Image Atlas* containing a suite of 31 gravity and magnetic image-maps at a scale of 1:250 000.

Tomography

3-D resistivity tomography has been adapted to investigate the heterogeneity of coastal sediments for the US Navy.

Slovakia, Jamaica and Papua New Guinea

A new project for the *International Decade for Natural Disaster Reduction* (IDNDR) is development of an implementation strategy for Landslide Hazard

Preparedness. The BGS has developed a prototype model for rapid landslide hazard assessment using remote sensing and GIS. The new study will define a generalised model and develop a strategy for practical implementation in developing countries.

Slovakia, Jamaica and Papua New Guinea present a range of scenarios for studying landslide hazards. These countries already have programmes concerned with landslide hazard assessment, and organisations there have expressed a strong interest in collaboration.

Hong Kong

Data from a nine-station seismic monitoring network installed for the Government's Geotechnical Office are helping to estimate regional seismic hazard.

Clay minerals played a key role in two landslips hosted by altered volcanic rocks in Hong Kong. Mineralogical and petrological studies commissioned by the Hong Kong Geotechnical Office showed that the tuffs are extensively replaced by the minerals halloysite and kaolinite, but the proportion of halloysite is significantly increased in fissures and surfaces associated with the landslips.

Interpolated In-Field Referencing (IIFR)

This new technique, developed to improve accuracy when directing well-bores towards geological targets, combines absolute measurements close to a drilling site with data from the UK observatories to enable the geomagnetic field to be specified accurately at any instant. IIFR continues to be used in drilling extended reach wells at Wytch Farm in Dorset, and was also applied west of Shetland where, for the first time, aeromagnetic survey data were used as traditional absolute observations cannot be made offshore.

Observatory Equipment

BGS-developed magnetic observatory systems were supplied to institutes in Brazil and Turkey. The BGS continues to assist developing countries to modernise their magnetic observatories; fluxgate magnetometers and logging equipment were donated to Mozambique.

Multicomponent Seismology

A novel shear-wave shock gun source for multicomponent surveys, developed in association with British Gas, was successfully tested. Sponsorship of the BGS Edinburgh Anisotropy Project increased to 14 companies. Techniques for assessing the sealing potential of faults in oil reservoirs, important for estimation of production capacity, were developed.

Mine Instability and Subsidence

Underground surveys undertaken at Force Crag Mine, to assess stability of mine workings, and the likely effect of collapse to the ground surface. Geochemical analysis of surface analysis of surface and underground water courses was also undertaken, commissioned by the National Trust.

Belgian Gravity Survey

A close-spaced regional gravity survey of 2740 square kilometres of Belgium, to the south-east of Brussels, was carried out under contract to the *Belgische Geologische Dienst* (Belgian Geological Survey).

Gypsum Subsidence

This ODA-supported study, to advise on planning for the avoidance of gypsum geohazards, is complete. It involved collaboration in China with the Institute of Hydrogeology and Engineering Geology, many provincial surveys and universities. Collaboration in Lithuania was with the Geological Survey of Lithuania and GROTA Hydrogeological Company.

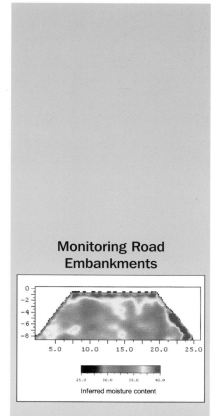

Monitoring Road Embankments

A non-invasive geophysical method (resistivity) has been developed and used to monitor seasonal changes in moisture within a road embankment. The high moisture contents seen on the right hand side of the diagram coincide with an area that failed shortly after this data was gathered.

L J Donnelly

Abandoned Mine Workings

The detection of these is an area of commercial activity, research and development. The picture shows abandoned near-surface workings in a modern clay opencast site near Sheffield.

The BGS investigates the sustainability, quality and management of groundwater resources both in the UK and overseas.

Groundwaters of the World

Support to the Palestinian Water Authority

The peace process in the Middle East brings with it many challenges, not least the management of scarce water resources. The BGS has provided technical expertise to the Palestinian Water Authority, concentrating on assessments of potential new water resources in Gaza and the management of West Bank water resources. BGS staff visited the West Bank to assist Palestinian counterparts with the preparation of a hydrogeological map which will be published in the summer of 1997. Analysis of remote sensed images will play an important role in this work.

Groundwater Pollution from Non-Agricultural Sources

Funded by the Environment Agency this project has reviewed existing literature related to the study of non-agricultural sources of nitrate and has proposed methods for identifying and quantifying such sources. These were tested against case studies using information provided by the EA.

Global Groundwater Scarcity

Water scarcity is increasingly a constraint to the development of many tropical countries. With ODA funding the BGS has carried out an assessment of water scarcity in Eastern and Southern Africa. Working with hydrologists from the Institute of Hydrology, existing meteorological, hydrological, hydrogeological and demographic data has been processed and used to derive indices of water scarcity for a grid of 50 kilometre square blocks. The information is accessible via a customised software package which can be used to assess both current water scarcity and the impacts of population growth and climate change.

Groundwater Management in Drought Prone Areas of Africa

This ODA-funded project studies ways in which the impact of groundwater drought can be alleviated for vulnerable communities. The work involves three partners: the Ghana Water and Sewerage Corporation, the Malawi Ministry of Irrigation and Water Development, and the South African Department of Water and Forestry. A major workshop on the project's findings was held in Lilongwe in February 1997.

OJU/LGA Benue State Water Supply Project, Nigeria

Oju Local Government Area is a remote part of south-eastern Nigeria that suffers from severe water shortage during the annual dry season *(below)*. The BGS has been subcontracted by WaterAid to provide specialist inputs into the ODA-funded Oju Water Supply, Sanitation and Health project. This project aims to provide 110 low cost, year-round, sustainable water sources to combat health problems, such as chronic guinea worm infection, amongst the local community.

A A McKenzie

Gauging station, Ain Sultan Spring, Jericho.

J Davies

Taking groundwater samples for hydrochemical analysis at Adiko, Oju, south eastern Nigeria: part of the Benue State Water Supply Project.

Risk to Deep Groundwaters from Urban Wastes

Groundwater is an important source of water supply for many cities in developing countries. Unfortunately the subsurface from which groundwater is obtained is also widely used for the disposal of wastewater. Consequently, shallow groundwater is frequently polluted beneath many unsewered cities. A simple methodology for assessing risk based on urban derived leakage, water quality change, and the likely impact has been developed with ODA funding.

Impact of Wastewater Reuse on Groundwater Quality in the Mezquital Valley

This joint project with the National Water Commission of Mexico is funded by the ODA. The overall objective of the study is to determine the effects of wastewater reuse on groundwater resources. Groundwater, soil sampling and drilling programmes have been established. The microbiological component of the study is being carried out by the London School of Hygiene and Tropical Medicine. Both positive impacts, in terms of additional recharge to groundwater resources, and negative impacts, in terms of groundwater quality, are being examined. The study will also establish methods for investigating such situations and build up the capabilities of the National Water Commission for carrying out such studies.

Development of New Well Siting Techniques — Electro Kinetic Sounding (EKS)

EKS experiments have continued in varied overseas hydrogeological regimes in support of the ODA-sponsored TDR Project to evaluate a new geophysical technique that is claimed to yield permeability/depth profiles and hence increase the success rate of boreholes in difficult environments. Work was carried out in Egypt, in the unconsolidated Nile Delta, and Zimbabwe in the shallow basement area near Bikita. Little correlation was found between promising EK sites and those found using other techniques (divining and conventional geophysics). Further experiments indicated the relationship between lateral seismic waves and the generation of electrical signals that was previously observed in the UK. Sites in Zimbabwe are due to be tested by drilling in June 1997.

Development of a Small Island Water Information System

Working with the Commonwealth Science Council, this project (funded by the ODA) plans to established mechanisms for information sharing between water sector professionals responsible for small island water management. A series of workshops to assess user priorities have been conducted and the project is moving on to establish a functional prototype system, concentrating on water quality issues, which will be tested with institutions in the Caribbean and Pacific.

Susceptibility Diagnostics

The costs of both aquifer and groundwater resource degradation can have significant impacts on local, regional and national economies. The diagnostic method resulting from this ODA-funded study will provide planners with a means of identifying those areas susceptible to undesirable side-effects of groundwater exploitation such as land-subsidence, saline intrusion and falling groundwater levels. The appropriate groundwater development strategies can be implemented.

Kamchatka

The objective of this project, funded by INTAS(EC)/SB, is to enable a multi-disciplinary scientific team from two centres of the Academy of Sciences, over 2500 kilometres apart, build an up-to-date portfolio of information on the hydrothermal areas of Kamchatka.

Vanuatu

ODA/BGS support was maintained for the Vanuatu Department of Geology, Mines and Water Resources, through the secondment of a Senior Hydrogeologist. A major responsibility of the department is the provision of data from boreholes for groundwater supplies for the rural communities.

Zimbabwe — Groundwater Recharge

A project is being carried out in collaboration with the Institute of Hydrology to investigate geochemical methods, in particular chloride balance, to allow regional estimates of groundwater recharge to be made in semi-arid regions. The BGS input has centred on the Romwe study catchment in the south of Zimbabwe, an area underlain by crystalline basement rock.

Environmental Arsenic Exposure: Health Risk and Geochemical Solutions

Exposure to arsenic from environmental sources, notably drinking water, food and soil, carries significant risks for human health. Much publicity has been given to the health problems associated with arsenic in groundwater in West Bengal and Bangladesh. This ODA-sponsored project has been established to investigate the processes involved in mobilisation of arsenic in groundwater, soils and sediments, to produce guidelines for the identification of susceptible groundwaters and develop methods for the remediation of aquifers and contaminated mining sites. Case studies of aquifers and mining areas are being undertaken in Argentina, Bangladesh and Thailand.

J Davies

Hyperkeratosis on the palms and feet is one common symptom of chronic arsenic poisoning, Ruppur village, Rajshahi District, Bangladesh.

Radiation and Waste

Radon Potential

BGS work on radon potential is being undertaken within the DoE research programme *Dealing with radon emissions in respect of new development* which is being carried out in collaboration with the BRE, NRPB and Land Use Consultants.

The variation in radon levels between different parts of the country is mainly controlled by the underlying geology. Geological radon potential indicates the probability that houses built on a specified geological unit will have radon concentrations exceeding the radon Action Level (200 Bq.m^{-3}) and can be used:

- to assess whether radon protective measures may be required in new buildings;

- for the cost-effective targeting of radon monitoring in existing dwellings and workplaces;

- to provide a radon assessment for home buyers and sellers through the BGS *Address-Linked Geological Inventory* (ALGI).

Minor Radiometric Contracts

Advice was provided on potential radon levels in new building developments in the Midlands and samples analysed for naturally radioactive elements by high resolution gamma-ray spectrometry. Modifications were made to a sea-bed gamma spectrometer system for the IAEA Marine Environmental Laboratory, Monaco.

Radioactivity in Groundwater

Research funded by the European Community and ODA has identified the presence of extremely high levels of uranium, radium and radon associated with two water supply wells in Amman, Jordan.

Characterisation of Pore Waters

Working for ANDRA *(Agence Nationale pour la gestion des Déchets Radioactifs)* and CEA *(Commissariat a l'Energie Atomique)* in France and with NAGRA *(Nationale Genossenschaft für die Lagerung radioactiver Abfälle)* in Switzerland, the BGS laboratories have used mechanical squeezing of core material and aqueous leaching of disaggregated core material, in combination with novel multi-variate statistical analysis of chemical data, to estimate pore-water composition.

Geomicrobiological Studies

Two studies were carried out for the *Power Reactor and Nuclear Fuel Development Corporation* (PNC) of Japan. The first examined the microbial effects on redox processes using experimental batch systems. The second study involved a biogeochemical assessment of the experimental Tono site in Japan using the BGS microbiological code *MGSE*.

Fluid Movement through Mudrocks

A theoretical and experimental study for the Swedish company SKB on the movement of repository gases in pre-compacted bentonite developed a quantified process model for application in safety assessment.

Effects of Humic Substances on the Migration of Radionuclides

The BGS is participating in an EC project aimed at understanding the effect of natural organic substances in groundwater on the complexation and transport of actinides: site-specific materials from proposed repositories within the European Community member states are being used.

3-D view of ^{137}Cs concentrations in the surface sediments of Morecambe Bay viewed from the south-west. The data were obtained by a hovercraft-borne radiometric survey as part of a MAFF-funded study of radionuclides in Irish Sea intertidal sediments. This provided the first detailed picture of radionuclides in the sediments of this area.

THE BGS AND NIREX

Core characterisation programme:
Mineralogical and petrological characterisation of drillcores from the Nirex deep geological site investigation at Sellafield, west Cumbria, revealed a complex history of fracture mineralisation. These studies have focused on evaluating the relationships between fracture mineralisation in the Borrowdale Volcanic Group (BVG), Carboniferous Limestone and Permo-Triassic strata, and the groundwater flow. Early pre-Carboniferous high temperature silicate-dominated hydrothermal mineralisation affects only the BVG. Calcite and dolomite represent the dominant fracture mineralisation and affect both the BVG basement and the Carboniferous to Triassic cover sequence. On the basis of petrographic, stable isotope and fluid inclusion observations, the carbonate vein mineralisation is identified as being syngenetic with deep burial diagenesis of the Permo-Triassic rocks. Late-stage iron and manganese oxyhydroxide mineralisation in the near surface rocks, and late-stage calcite mineralisation at depth correlate closely with zones of present-day groundwater flow. The morphology of the late-stage calcite *(see right)* varies systematically with the salinity of the present-day groundwater and provides a potential means of monitoring changes in deep groundwater composition during the Quaternary.

Detailed petrological studies showed that a zone of intense alteration in the BVG of the Sellafield area resulted from early mineralogical and chemical alteration, possibly in a geothermal system related to volcanism. The zone of alteration was later a focus for intense cleavage formation and pervasive hematitisation and affected the distribution of later veining.

Lithostratigraphy and structure:
a new lithostratigraphy, based on examination of borehole core and temporary sections, was defined for the Quaternary deposits of West Cumbria. This has both assisted the correlation of onshore and offshore sequences and has given a better appreciation of vertical and lateral variations.

A major revision of the geological structure of the Sellafield Site was undertaken and presented as revised Reference Drawings. Draft text was completed for the co-funded West Cumbria memoir. A structural atlas of discontinuity data from the Sellafield boreholes was completed and the work presented at the EUG and the Geological Society of London.

Rock mass research: the 3-D spatial heterogeneity of rock mass properties around the Sellafield site was studied by bringing together wireline, core and 3-D seismic attribute information. This work resulted in improved determination of geomechanical properties from wireline logs and greater understanding of the relationship between rock stress and the anisotropy of fracture permeability. In particular, significant advances have been made in the prediction of permeability and porosity, and the extrapolation of these properties into three dimensions via linkages to 3-D seismic data.

NIREX Core Characterisation Programme

a

b

(a) SEM micrograph of late-stage calcite with c-axis elongated crystal morphology from within the saline groundwater zone. (b) SEM micrograph of late-stage calcite with nailhead crystal morphology, syngenetic with calcite in (a), from within the freshwater zone.

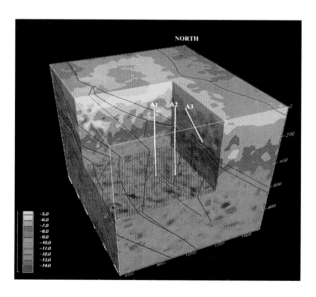

Rock mass research: *3-D distribution of estimated permeability between two contrasting lithologies derived from wireline, core and seismic information.*

The National Geosciences Information Service provides access to, and data and advice from, collections of bibliographic and cartographic material, records, samples, and digital databases.

Records and Databases

Collections Administration

A complete replacement of the records storage system at Keyworth with customised mobile racking has greatly increased to capacity for records storage. Despite the considerable disruption to the Records Room, special provision was made for visitors and BGS staff and all data remained available for consultation.

A major project to index, validate and database all the mine plans held in Keyworth was completed with 10 000 plans databased.

In addition, drillcore and specimens from a further 195 onshore boreholes were added to the national archive; the largest volume of material being derived from bores drilled in the 1970s/1980s by the predecessors of the NRA and Severn Trent Water in the Cheshire Basin area.

Information Systems

This activity is primarily concerned with the maintenance and development of corporate information systems including data architecture, databases, geographical information systems (GIS), software applications and CD-ROM and other forms of electronic publication. Today, all aspects of the BGS's, activities depend to greater or lesser extent on information systems which, in turn, rely on modern and cost-effective information technology. The BGS has invested heavily in moving from its 1980s style VAX-based computing to a state-of-the-art distributed PC and UNIX network, most of which was completed by the end of the financial year.

Continuing work on BGS's advanced 1:10 000-scale digital mapping production system has involved maintenance and consolidation, and for the future, initial work has been completed on the development of object-oriented publication system.

IT is increasingly a fundamental component of BGS's overseas work as well as its UK activities and IT specialists contributed significantly to projects in Papua New Guinea, Nigeria and elsewhere.

Geological Map Data

Work began on the conversion of the 1:250 000-scale chronostratigraphical and lithological database of Great Britain to lithostratigraphy, with first proof stage being reached by the end of the year. The lithostratigraphical database at 1:50 000 scale, which grows steadily during normal digital map production, was given a boost by the digitisation of existing printed maps in some areas; particularly in south east England with the addition of maps digitised for Kent CC under a data licensing deal.

Borehole Database

Additional staff have been recruited to eliminate the backlog of borehole records awaiting registration in Keyworth and Edinburgh within five years. In this first year a total of 101 523 boreholes were processed and indexed, reducing the backlog by 60 988 (26 per cent).

The publication of the British Borehole Index with search software on CD ROM has generated considerable commercial

T P Cullen

Retrieving drill core from the National Core Store at the BGS.

interest. There have been a significant number of additional requests for records as a result of this product.

The transfer of released onshore hydrocarbon drillcore and cuttings from DTI Edinburgh Core Store to Keyworth is now complete. BGS now holds the most comprehensive set of released onshore UK hydrocarbon material outside that held by the operators.

In addition, drillcore and specimens from a further 195 onshore boreholes were added to the national archive; the largest volume of material being derived from bores drilled in the 1970s/1980s by the predecessors of the NRA and Severn Trent Water in the Cheshire Basin area.

Groundwater Data Management System for Developing Countries

All groundwater projects require access to archives of groundwater data. Accurate well records are vital for effective project planning and to avoid the repetition of costly mistakes. In many countries insufficient attention is paid to the management of national well archives. Contrasting data management experiences from different countries were reviewed, to allow the preparation of guidelines on groundwater data management for project managers and water resource planners. The results of the project, funded by the ODA, were presented at a workshop in Malawi and a prototype of a new groundwater data management system was installed at the Ministry of Irrigation and Water Development in Lilongwe.

BritRocks Database

Development of the BGS petrological sample collections has passed two important milestones with the introduction of flexible computer-based search and access services. The new BritRocks database has been equipped with a multi-user PC-based interface for access to more than 150 000 rock samples and thin sections in the BGS petrological reference collections. In addition, some 14 000 samples of building stones and other commercially worked stones from the regional collections have been assembled in an additional database in order to open up this extensive resource to the user community.

Geochemistry Database

The Geochemistry Database now holds over five million analyses and incorporates rock, drillcore, stream sediment, panned concen-

trate, water and soil data collected as part of the G-BASE and Minerals Programmes. A user-friendly, front-end interface is now being extended to a GIS interface allowing interactive searches by area.

Landslide Database

A landslide database designed for recording slope instability information during applied geological mapping of the City of Bradford Metropolitan District, has been further developed to record and retrieve information on landslides encountered during other Core and Commissioned mapping surveys. The database currently holds information on c. 250 landslides identified during mapping in West Yorkshire, including locational and other details pertaining to slope, geology, groundwater, landslide dimensions, movement type and state of activity. Population of the database is ongoing as mapping programmes progress.

ALGI

During the year, the ALGI (*Address-Linked Geological Inventory*) system was developed to enable the rapid production of cheap, computer-generated geological reports (*below*). ALGI coverage of the Bristol area was completed in March, ready for a public launch in April 1997. There has been considerable interest in the ALGI product from conveyancing solicitors concerned about ground condition problems which may affect properties. Completion of ALGI coverage for the London area (within the M25) is scheduled for August 1997.

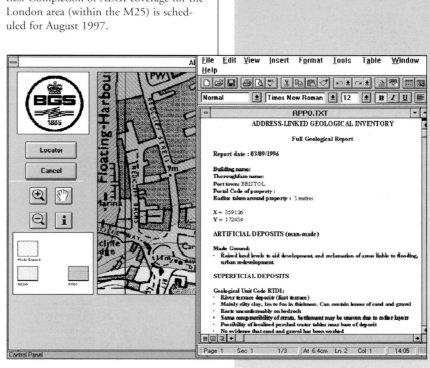

Screen image of the ALGI report-generating system.

Science for All

Popular publications.

Publications

These are listed in Appendix 3 and included the following:

- 29 new 1: 50 000 scale maps to advance copy release in digital and plot-on-demand form

- 31 new 1:50 000 scale maps to release in printed form

- two 1:250 000 scale maps

- three new *Memoirs* and a new *Regional Guide* (London and the Thames Valley)

- *Earthwise* magazines on the International Arena and the Coastal Zone.

Popular Publications

More publications were produced under the BGS's *Earthwise* label:

- another *Fossil Focus* card — Ostracods

- two more *Holiday Geology Guides*-Trafalgar Square and Heritage in Stone: Nottingham

- the first *Holiday Geology Map* — Isle of Wight

- an innovative book — *Yorkshire Rock: a journey through time.*

Customer Services

New information leaflets and catalogues continue to be produced to promote new products. The new *Regional Catalogue of Books and Maps* with a print run of 5 000 has been particularly successful. Emphasis has been placed on promoting the more popularly oriented *Earthwise* publications through advertisements in magazines and the distribution of review copies to a wide range of newspapers, magazines and journals.

A *Friends of BGS* scheme has been introduced during the year. Membership of this scheme enables the public to keep up to date with the activities of the BGS. It is open to both individuals and institutions, including school teachers, retired employees, amateur geologists, libraries and museums.

Revised interactive Sales and Product data are now available on the Internet.

Information & Advice

During the year approximately 24 000 enquiries were handled, providing a comprehensive service to members of the public, industry and geoscience users.

The number of site specific enquiries continued to rise and were 20 per cent up on the previous year totalling over 4 000, which were handled within the customer response targets.

The number of chargeable enquiries has increased by 10 per cent and there has been a corresponding increase in the total income derived from enquiries of 12 per cent

Library

The first phase of work on a digital index to the photograph collections in the Library has been completed, providing access to over 60 000 photographs in the BGS, British Association and other collections. A bid has been submitted to the Knowledge Gallery initiative for funding to scan a selection of photographs which will be held as thumbnail sketches in the digital index.

Map & Publication Sales

The total number of BGS Approved Stockists now includes 58 retail book and map resellers and eight regional wholesalers. In addition, some 40 Stationery Office bookshops and agents also supply BGS publications to end-users.

Digital Data Sales

Two *Value Added Reseller* agreements were signed during the year, enabling companies to incorporate BGS data within their value added products.

Copyright

Enforcing the Survey's rights under the Copyright Act remained a priority. Over 50 requests for permission to use BGS materials are being processed per month by the Copyright Manager, and copyright income increased by 40 per cent over the year.

Dynamic Earth

During the year Dr S K Monro was appointed, on a consultancy basis, as Scientific Director of *The Dynamic Earth,* a major millenium-funded exhibition.

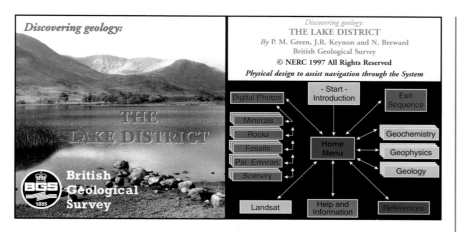

This new CD-ROM uses digital imagery, photographs and explanatory text to provide an overview of the geology, geochemistry and scenery of the Lake District. It is designed for educational users from Key Stage 4 to Degree and University research levels, and for earth and environmental scientists and anyone interested in the Lake District.

Public Relations

A large number of guided tours continued to be given of the Keyworth site, along with an introduction to the history and current role of the BGS, to a variety of groups and individuals. In addition to site visits, the BGS fulfills its important function to promote earth science in the general and educational community in a variety of other ways, notably:

- Responding to the numerous requests for information on the history and role of the BGS and careers in earth science;

- Giving (on request) external lectures and talks to a variety of community and education groups on a diverse range of earth science related topics;

- Attending careers fairs with information on the BGS and the earth sciences in general, e.g .in the Lincoln area —*What next at 16+?*

- Participating in NERC Schools Liaison Committee activities.

- Contributing to national events. *National Science, Engineering and Technology Week* (SET 97) was again supported by the BGS Keyworth in March this year. The programme of events was greatly expanded. The interactive displays and talks for primary school children also featured a dramatic performance by students from Nottingham's Clarendon College entitled *'Shaping the Planet'*.

Training

- In October, BGS successfully attained the *Investors in People* national standard, linking training and staff development to business objectives.

- The drive towards Professional Accreditation of staff continued; over a quarter of scientific staff have now attained chartered status.

- BGS staff attended over 127 in-house and other training courses.

- Several new courses were brought on-stream, including: *Modern Volcanism (Santorini); Introduction to Petroleum Geology; Geology for non-Geologists; Chemical Speciation;* and *Introduction to Visual Modflow.*

- An NVQ programme was initiated and about 10 per cent of staff continue in some form of Further Education.

- The first cohort of a new MSc., *Computing for Geoscience,* which is jointly taught by the BGS and Nottingham Trent University, successfully completed the course. Information Systems staff were instrumental in the course design and contributed to the teaching, along with other BGS specialists.

- Four study attachments, totalling 28 man-weeks, catered for colleagues from Jordan and Nigeria. These included training in techniques for radiochemical analysis, x-ray diffraction analysis, environmental geochemistry and in remote sensing and image analysis.

Press

The Press Office continued to fill a vital role in the promotion of BGS and its activities. During 1996–97 it was responsible for 88 news releases. It dealt with more than 400 unsolicited media enquiries, resulting in nearly 16 000 single-column centimetres of press coverage (with a value of more than third of a million pounds) in newspapers and magazines outside the educational press. 60 television and radio broadcasts were arranged.

During the year the Press Office ratified the Media Liaison Network, further developed *Earthnews,* the monthly summary of news releases, and launched a monthly in-house diary to allow future event-planning to be more circumspect. It also set up cooperative links with colleagues in the Geological Society.

In cooperation with the BGS Public Relations team, the Press Office took an active part in organising the De la Beche bicentennial celebrations held at the Natural History Museum in November.

Appendix 1   Organisation in 1996†

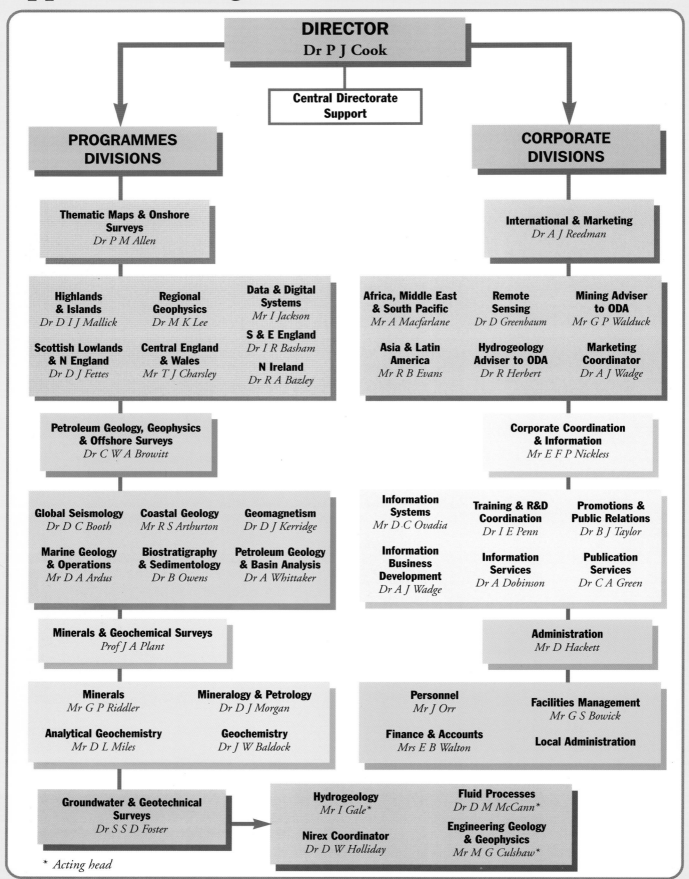

DIRECTOR
Dr P J Cook

Central Directorate Support

PROGRAMMES DIVISIONS

Thematic Maps & Onshore Surveys
Dr P M Allen

Highlands & Islands Dr D I J Mallick	**Regional Geophysics** Dr M K Lee	**Data & Digital Systems** Mr I Jackson
Scottish Lowlands & N England Dr D J Fettes	**Central England & Wales** Mr T J Charsley	**S & E England** Dr I R Basham
		N Ireland Dr R A Bazley

Petroleum Geology, Geophysics & Offshore Surveys
Dr C W A Browitt

Global Seismology Dr D C Booth	**Coastal Geology** Mr R S Arthurton	**Geomagnetism** Dr D J Kerridge
Marine Geology & Operations Mr D A Ardus	**Biostratigraphy & Sedimentology** Dr B Owens	**Petroleum Geology & Basin Analysis** Dr A Whittaker

Minerals & Geochemical Surveys
Prof J A Plant

Minerals Mr G P Riddler	**Mineralogy & Petrology** Dr D J Morgan
Analytical Geochemistry Mr D L Miles	**Geochemistry** Dr J W Baldock

Groundwater & Geotechnical Surveys
Dr S S D Foster

Hydrogeology Mr I Gale*	**Fluid Processes** Dr D M McCann*
Nirex Coordinator Dr D W Holliday	**Engineering Geology & Geophysics** Mr M G Culshaw*

CORPORATE DIVISIONS

International & Marketing
Dr A J Reedman

Africa, Middle East & South Pacific Mr A Macfarlane	**Remote Sensing** Dr D Greenbaum	**Mining Adviser to ODA** Mr G P Walduck
Asia & Latin America Mr R B Evans	**Hydrogeology Adviser to ODA** Dr R Herbert	**Marketing Coordinator** Dr A J Wadge

Corporate Coordination & Information
Mr E F P Nickless

Information Systems Mr D·C Ovadia	**Training & R&D Coordination** Dr I E Penn	**Promotions & Public Relations** Dr B J Taylor
Information Business Development Dr A J Wadge	**Information Services** Dr A Dobinson	**Publication Services** Dr C A Green

Administration
Mr D Hackett

Personnel Mr J Orr	**Facilities Management** Mr G S Bowick
Finance & Accounts Mrs E B Walton	**Local Administration**

* Acting head

† *In January 1997 a new organisation structure was implemented and was fully operational by 1 April 1997.*

Appendix 2   Finance

BGS EXPENDITURE — 1996/97

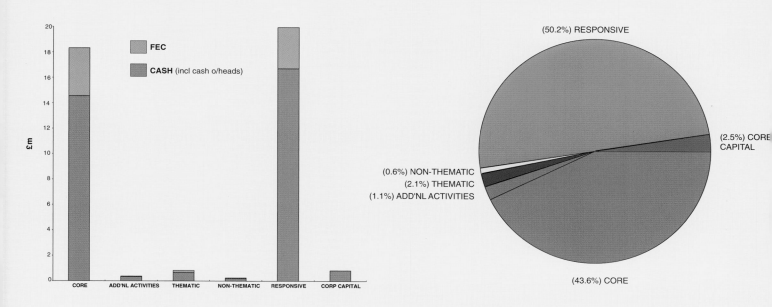

SOURCES OF BGS INCOME 1991/92 — 1996/97
(at 1996/97 prices — £m)

	1991/92	1992/93	1993/94	1994/95	1995/96	1996/97
Science Budget	£12.82	£14.23	£13.10	£13.01	£13.95	£15.15
Government	£13.31	£10.04	£7.35	£6.48	£6.33	£6.37
Other	£8.93	£9.13	£9.66	£10.62	£13.08	£11.86

(1) 1995/96 onwards includes superannuation. Previously superannuation was treated as an indirect cost.

(2) Figures for 1996/97 are based on March final data.

Appendix 3   Publishing

Interim issue of maps

To ensure the earliest possible release of current geological data to the public, all new 1:50 000 maps are first made available in digital form and as electrostatic plots (on-demand), in advance of litho printing. The purchase of an electrostatic plot entitles the customer to a free copy of the printed map if and when this is published.

MAPS PUBLISHED

The following abbreviations are used throughout: S – solid; D – drift; S&D – solid and drift; SwD – solid with drift; S,D – both editions on one sheet; Q – Quaternary; PQ – Pre-Quaternary; † – provisional edition.

1:1 500 000

Metallogenic map of Britain and Ireland

1:1 000 000

Industrial mineral resources map of Britain

1:250 000

Moray Firth S
Wight S

1:50 000 (PRINTED)

ENGLAND AND WALES

104	Mablethorpe † S&D
116	Skegness † S&D
126	Nottingham S&D
127	Grantham S&D
168	Birmingham S&D
176	Lowestoft S&D
191	Saxmundham S&D
257	Romford S&D
297	Wincanton S&D
317/332	Chichester & Bognor S&D

SCOTLAND

5W	Kircudbright
9E	Thornhill S
12	Campbeltown † S&D
20	Sound of Gigha † S&D
24E	Peebles S
27	North Islay † S&D
28W	South Jura † S&D
28E	Knapdale † S&D
35	Colonsay † S&D
43N	Staffa † S&D
65E	Ballater S
66W	Aboyne S

73E	Foyers S
75W	Glenlivet S
82E	Scardroy † S&D
85E	Glenfiddich S
86E	Turriff S&D
115W	Strathy Point † S&D

NORTHERN IRELAND

33	Omagh S&D

COASTAL GEOLOGY – England and Wales

263, 279, 295   Inner Bristol Channel and Severn Estuary PQ&Q
263, 279, 295   Inner Bristol Channel and Severn Estuary PQ

1:50 000 (ELECTROSTATIC PLOT)

ENGLAND AND WALES

10	Newbiggin S, S&D
23	Cockermouth S&D
23	Cockermouth S
35/44	Whitby & Scalby † S&D
40	Kirkby Stephen † S&D
41	Richmond † S&D
47	Bootle S, S&D
48	Ulverston S&D
48	Ulverston S
50	Hawes † S&D
119	Snowdon S&D
126	Nottingham S&D
129	The Wash S&D
168	Birmingham S&D
270	South London S&D
278/294	Minehead S&D

SCOTLAND

6W	Kirkbean S
6W	Kirkbean S&D
9W	New Galloway S
22W/21E	Irvine S
24E	Peebles S
28E	Knapdale † S&D
56W	Glen Shee S
67	Stonehaven S&D
85E	Glenfiddich S
91/100	Gairloch † S&D
101W	Summer Isles † S&D
103E	Helmsdale † S&D
113	Cape Wrath † S&D

BOOKS PUBLISHED

ANNUAL REPORT

Report for 1995/96

SHEET MEMOIRS

ENGLAND AND WALES

199   Worcester

SCOTLAND

84W   Fortrose
31W   Airdrie

LITHOSTRATIGRAPHIC ATLAS

North-West Margin, Vol. 1

SPECIAL BOOKS

Hydrogeology of Northern Ireland

TECHNICAL REPORTS

WA/96/1   A geological background for planning and development in the City of Bradford Metropolitan District. 2 Vols.
WN/94/31 Engineering geology of rocks and soils: Gault Clay
WQ/96/1   Science in a market economy
WQ/96/3   Societal trends and their impact on the coastal zone and adjacent seas
WQ/97/1   The role of the earth in sustaining our life-support system

BRITISH REGIONAL GEOLOGY

London and the Thames Valley

MINERAL RESOURCES

United Kingdom minerals yearbook 1996
World mineral statistics 1991–95

MAGAZINES

Earthwise, Issues 8 and 9
ODA Earthworks, Issue 9

POPULAR PUBLICATIONS

Discovering geology card — Fossil focus: *Ostracods*
Holiday geology guide — Heritage in stone: *Nottingham*
Holiday geology guide — *Trafalgar Square*
Holiday geology map — *Isle of Wight*
Yorkshire Rock: a journey through time

REPRINTS

Memoir — The geology of the South Wales Coalfield: Pontypridd and Maesteg

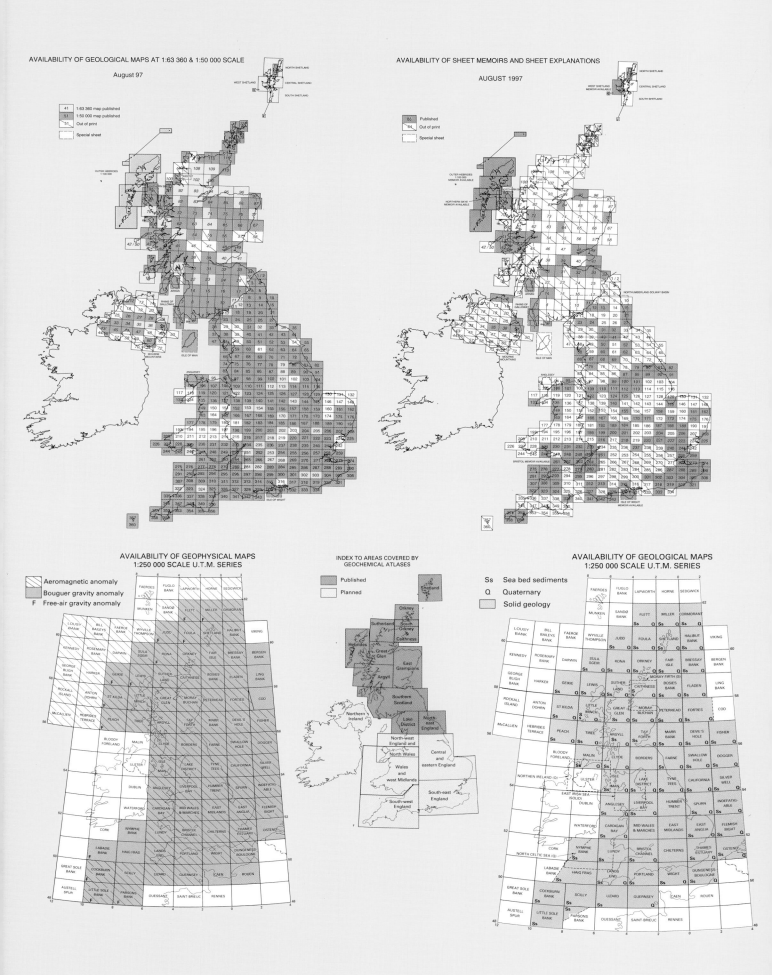

AVAILABILITY OF GEOLOGICAL MAPS AT 1:63 360 & 1:50 000 SCALE

August 97

41 1:63 360 map published
51 1:50 000 map published
51 Out of print
□ Special sheet

AVAILABILITY OF SHEET MEMOIRS AND SHEET EXPLANATIONS

AUGUST 1997

88 Published
64 Out of print
□ Special sheet

AVAILABILITY OF GEOPHYSICAL MAPS
1:250 000 SCALE U.T.M. SERIES

▨ Aeromagnetic anomaly
▦ Bouguer gravity anomaly
F Free-air gravity anomaly

INDEX TO AREAS COVERED BY
GEOCHEMICAL ATLASES

▨ Published
□ Planned

AVAILABILITY OF GEOLOGICAL MAPS
1:250 000 SCALE U.T.M. SERIES

Ss Sea bed sediments
Q   Quaternary
▨   Solid geology

TECHNICAL REPORTS
(made available by the authors' group)

Onshore Geology

WA/92/70 The stratigraphy and structure of the Skiddaw Group in the Black Combe inlier: Geological notes to accompany 1:25 sheet SD18.

WA/93/56 Geology of the Crofton area. 1:10 000 sheet SE31NE. Part of 1:50 000 sheets 78 (Wakefield).

WA/93/57 Geology of the Hemsworth area. 1:10 000 Sheet SE41SW. Part of 1:50 000 Sheets 78 (Wakefield) and 87 (Barnsley).

WA/93/73 Geology of the Hillam area. 1:10 000 sheet SE52NW. Part of 1:50 000 sheets 78 (Wakefield).

WA/93/74 Geology of the Sherburn in Elmet and Biggin district. 1:10 000 sheets SE43SE and SE53SW. Part of 1:50 000 sheets 70 (Leeds) and 78 (Wakefield).

WA/93/75 Geology of the Upton area. 1:10 000 sheet SE41SE. Part of 1:50 000 sheets 78 (Wakefield) and 87 (Barnsley).

WA/93/76 Geology of the Wentbridge area. 1:10 000 sheet SE41NE. Part of 1:50 000 sheet 78 (Wakefield).

WA/94/28 Geological notes and local details for 1:10 000 sheets SU28SE, SU92SW and SU92SE (Midhurst, Lodsworth and Petworth). Parts of 1:50 000 sheets 301 (Haslemere) and 317 (Chichester).

WA/95/106 Geological notes and local details for 1:10 000 sheet SP01SW (Colesbourne). Part of 1:50 000 sheet 235 (Cirencester).

WA/95/107 Geological notes and local details for 1:10 000 Sheet SP01NW (Andoversford). Part of 1:50 000 Sheet 235 (Cirencester).

WA/95/111 The revision of the Richmond (41) 1:50 000 Provisional Geological sheet: data sources, interpretation, additional geological and geophysical information.

WA/95/85 Geology of the Great Ridge–Hindon district (Wiltshire). 1:10 000 sheets ST 93 NW (Great Ridge) and ST 93 SW (Hindon). Part of 1:50 000 sheets 297 (Wincanton) and 298 (Salisbury).

WA/95/86 Geology of the Heytesbury district (Wiltshire) 1:10 000 sheet ST94SW (Heytesbury). Part of 1:50 000 sheets 281 (Frome), 282 (Devizes), 297 (Wincanton) and 298 (Salisbury).

WA/95/91 Geology of the Fettercairn area. 1:10 000 sheets NO67SW, NO67NE, NO67SW, NO67SE and NO68SE (South of the Highland Boundary Fault). Part of 1:50 000 sheets 66E (Banchory), 66W (Aboyne), 57W (Forfar) and 57E (Montrose).

WA/96/1 A geological background for planning and development in the City of Bradford Metropolitan District. Volume 1: A guide to the use of earth science information in planning and development.

WA/96/1 A geological background for planning and development in the City of Bradford Metropolitan District. Volume 2: A technical guide to ground conditions.

WA/96/10 Geology of the Wakefield South area: 1:10 000 sheet SE31NW. Part of 1:50 000 sheet 78 (Wakefield).

WA/96/11 Geology of the Swadlincote and Church Gresley districts. 1:10 000 sheets SK31NW and SK21NE. Part of 1:50 000 sheet 141 (Loughborough), 155 (Coalville), 154 (Lichfield) and 140 (Burton).

WA/96/13 Geological description of the Carboniferous outcrop on the Peebles Sheet (24E).

WA/96/17 Geology of the Ossett area.

WA/96/18 Geology of the Wakefield North area.

WA/96/2 Geology of the Ashby-de-la-Zouch district. 1:10 000 sheet SK31NE. Part of 1:50 000 sheets 141 (Loughborough) and 155 (Coalville).

WA/96/22 Geology of the Gass Water area. Explanation of 1:10 000 sheet NS62SE. Part of 1:50 000 sheet 15W (New Cumnock).

WA/96/28 Geology of the Craigdullyeart area. Explanation of 1:10 000 sheet NS61NE. Part of 1:50 000 sheet 15W (New Cumnock).

WA/96/32 Selected geological locality details for the Minehead district. 1:50 000 sheet 278 and part of sheet 294.

WA/96/40 Geology of the Ilkley, Burley In Wharfedale, Middleton Moor and Timble areas.

WA/96/49 Geology of the Newton Poppleford district (Devon). 1:10 000 sheet SY08NE. Part of 1:50 000 sheets 325 (Exeter), 339 (Newton Abbot) and 326/340 (Sidmouth and Otterton).

WA/96/53 SJ60 and parts of SJ61, SJ70 and SJ71. Telford (Quaternary and recent strata). Part of 1:50 000 sheets 152 (Shrewsbury) and 153 (Wolverhampton).

WA/96/55 Geology of the country to the north of Bishops Waltham, East Hampshire district. 1:10 000 sheets SU51NE, SU52SE and parts of SU51NW and SU52SW. Part of the 1:50 000 geological sheets 316 (Fareham) and 300 (Alresford).

WA/96/65 Geology of the area between Petersfield and Rowlands Castle, Hampshire and West Sussex. 1:10 000 sheets SU71SW, SU71NW and part of SU72SW. Part of 1:50 000 geological sheet 316 (Fareham).

WA/96/67 Geology of the South Harting, Compton and West Marden district, West Sussex. 1:10 000 sheets SU71NE, 71SE and part of SU72SE. Part of 1:50 000 geological sheet 316 (Fareham).

WA/96/68 Geology of the Findochty and Bin of Cullen areas. 1:10 000 sheets NJ46NE, NJ46SE and part of NJ45NE. Part of 1:50 000 sheet Scotland 96W (Portsoy).

WA/96/7 Geology of the lower Derwent valley: 1:10 000 sheets SK33SE, 43SW and 43SE. Part of 1:50 000 sheets 141 (Loughborough).

WA/96/70 Geology of the Warnford and Droxford district, Hampshire.

WA/96/9 Geology of the Horbury area: 1:10 000 sheet SE21NE. Part of 1:50 000 sheet 77 (Huddersfield) and 78 (Wakefield).

Marine Geology

WB/95/35 The Wight 1:250 000 — scale solid geology sheet (2nd edition).

WB/95/42 Catalogue of available BGS marine reports and publications without confidential titles.

WB/96/25 Field report on the 1996 LOIS-LOEPS Humber Estuary Intertidal Coring.

WB/96/28 High-resolution seismic surveys in the region of the Traendjupet slide off Mid-Norway. Meteor cruise 36/3, 21/7/96–17/08/96.

WB/96/32 Geologic: Software package for logging and plotting borehole data. User guide.

WB/96/6 Laboratory Report on core collected, MAST Hammer Corer trials. Firth of Forth.

Overseas Geology

WC/94/3 Final Report on stream sediment, soil and forage chemistry as indicators of cattle mineral status in North-East Zimbabwe.

WC/95/14 The development and validation of a method for the determination of aluminium in natural waters.

WC/95/52 Sustainable groundwater development of Hard-Rock Aquifers: The conflict between irrigation and drinking water supplies from the Deccan Basalts of India.

WC/95/62 Radiometric measurements, soil and water sampling in tin mining areas of Malaysia.

WC/95/71 Unconsolidated sedimentary aquifers: Review no. 7 — Remote sensing methods.

WC/96/1 Geoscience databases and related coastal zone management issues.

WC/96/10 Unconsolidated sedimentary aquifers: Review No. 10 — Applications of surface and airborne geophysics.

WC/96/14 Geoscientific databases and related coastal zone management issues: Project Summary Report.

WC/96/15 Trial surveys with the Electro-Kinetic survey technique in the Red River Basin of Vietnam.

WC/96/2 The Red River Delta of Vietnam: A demonstration of the applicability of sedimentology to the investigation of unconsolidated sedimentary aquifers.

WC/96/22 The effect of urbanisation on the groundwater quality beneath the city of Hanoi, Vietnam.

WC/96/25 Groundwater management in drought prone areas of Africa Northern Ghana — Inception Report.

WC/96/28 Groundwater management in drought prone areas of Africa. Malawi Inception Report.

WC/96/34 Yao Ba Oasis environment project, China Project Final Report.

WC/96/37 Assessment of contamination by metals and selected organic compounds in coastal sediments and waters of Mombasa, Kenya.

WC/96/38 The computer simulation of the movement of the saline groundwater at Yao Ba Oasis, Inner Mongolia.

WC/96/39 Unconsolidated sedimentary aquifers: Review No. 12 — Groundwater Quality Management in unconsolidated sedimentary aquifers.

WC/96/41 A Geographic Information System (GIS) for environmental management of the Mombasa coast, Kenya.

WC/96/6 Groundwater development in unconsolidated sedimentary aquifers: A Developer's Aid (Version 2).

WC/96/8 Unconsolidated sedimentary aquifers: Special study No. 1 — Study of causes of borehole deterioration, Pakistan.

WC/96/9 Unconsolidated sedimentary aquifers: Review No. 9 — Irrigation.

Hydrogeology

WD/94/57 The application of hydrogeochemical data and maps for environmental interpretation in Upland Britain.

WD/95/15 Mineralisation of shallow fracture surfaces in the chalk and implications for contamination attenuation.

WD/95/22 Estimating groundwater recharge through glacial till at Bacon Hall, Shropshire.

WD/95/61 Estimating groundwater recharge through clays-with-flints using data from drain gauges at Rothamsted.

WD/95/66 Development of a rapid method for determining apparent diffusion coefficients for chloride in chalk.

WD/96/26 The use of Environmental Tracers in chalk Hydrogeology.

WD/96/3 The effect of drought on the availability of groundwater: towards an analytical framework.

WD/96/31 Geophysical logging at West Newton Grange, Golden Square Wood, West End Farm Kilham, and Ella

Crossroads boreholes, Yorkshire on behalf of the North East Region, Environment Agency.

WD/96/69 Kamchatka — Scientific investigation, protection and management of unique hydrothernal phenomena. Intas project 94–1592.

WD/96/8 Groundwater resources degradation in Jersey: Socio-economic impacts and their mitigation.

Fluid Processes

WE/93/4 Geochemical validation of solute residence times: a review of the scientific basis for dating groundwaters.

WE/94/24 Characterisation of superficial Clay-with-Flint.

WE/95/1 Investigation of changes in gas composition during subsurface migration from the Foxhall Landfill, Suffolk —Phase II.

WE/95/37 Hydrogeological and Hydrochemical studies of the Lowestoft Till, East Anglia.

WE/95/41 The influence of Microbes on the rates of Aqueous reactions in mid-ocean ridge hydrothermal systems.

WE/95/50 Fate of organic pollutants in groundwaters around landfill sites.

WE/95/7 The response of a migrating gas plume to gas extraction from the Foxhill Landfill, Suffolk

WE/96/1 Mechanisms and rates of recharge through glacial till: Experimental and modelling studies from a Norfolk site.

WE/96/26 Computer modelling of Microbial processes using MGSE — an Overview. (Microbial growth in subsurface environments).

WE/96/35 Possible anthropogenic pertubations within a lake sediment core from Wastwater.

WE/96/6 The hydrogeology and hydrochemistry of glacial till and glacio-lacustrine sediments in Shropshire.

Mineralogy and Petrology

WG/95/31 The petrology and provenance of the Lower Old Red Sandstone, New Cumnock (Sheet 15W) Scotland.

WG/96/10 The structure and petrology of shear zones and associated rocks in the Strathnairn District, (Sheet 74 W), Monadhliath Mountains, Scotland.

WG/96/11 Petrography of Namurian rock samples from the Bradford area (10 sheet 69). March 1996.

WG/96/18 The Darwin collection: Galapagos Archipelago.

WG/96/24 Petrology, geochemistry and classification of the Clyde Plateau volcanic formation, Kilmarnock district (sheet 22), Midland Valley, Scotland.

WG/96/26 The Minerology and Petrology of the Igneous and Metaphorphic rocks exposed in the Macduff district. (Sheet 96E), Northeast Scotland.

WG/96/3 Mineralogical characteristics of samples of clay-with-flints.

WG/96/31 Petrography of Namurian rock samples from the Bradford area: 2. (1:50 000).

WG/96/32 The Minerology and Petrology of the igneous rocks exposed within the Livingston district (Sheet 32W), Midland Valley, Scotland.

WG/96/4 Mineralogical characteristics of samples of Shropshire till.

WG/96/5 A Batch Processing Framework for automated Petrographic Image Analysis.

WG/96/9 Regional low grade metamorphism in the Plymouth district, 1:50 000 geological sheet 348.

Analytical Geochemistry

WI/95/15 Organic geochemical studies in Wolverhampton.

WI/95/16 Microcosm experiments to study Isoproturon degradation in a United Kingdom chalk aquifer.

Regional Geophysics

WK/92/9 Geophysical evidence for the form of the New Red Sandstone basins in the Exeter district.

WK/96/1 BREDUC — a computer program for the reduction of UK land gravity data.

Global Seismology

WL/93/23 Linear matrix operations for multicomponent seismic processing.

WL/95/34 The Coniston earthquake of 18 July 1994 (2.2ML).

WL/95/35 The Newtown earthquake of 17 March 1994 (3.1 ML).

WL/96/11 Reservoir characterisation: how can anisotropy help?

WL/96/12 On the quality of intensity assignments from historical earthquake data.

WL/96/14 Seismic monitoring of mining-induced earthquakes during the closing stages of production at Bilston Glen Colliery, Midlothian, 1987–1990.

WL/96/18 Earthquake prediction studies in the Yanqing–Huailai Basin.

WL/96/19 The mean transmission properties of a fault with imperfect facial contact.

WL/96/21 The Barrow-in-Furness earthquake of 15 February 1865: liquefaction from a very small magnitude event.

WL/96/22 On the evaluation Macroseismic scales.

WL/96/23 Automatic picking seismic arrivals from single component recordings using a back-propagation neural network.

WL/96/24 Application of back-propagation neural networks to identification of seismic arrivals types.

WL/96/25 Seismic hazard studies in the UK: Methodological problems of Intraplate systems.

WL/96/3 Roots and references for the UK Earthquake catalogue.

WL/96/7 Effects of learning parameters on learning procedure and performance of a BPNN. April 1996.

Geomagnetism

WM/95/26 Operating instructions for an observatory D/I Fluxgate Theodolite Magnetometer.

WM/95/31 Fluxgate Logging Automatic Recording Equipment (FLARE).

WM/95/32 The BGS Proton Magnetometer (deltaD/deltaI) Observatory System Mark II Installation Guide and Technical Manual.

WM/ES/95/12 Eskdalemuir monthly bulletin — December 1995.

WM/ES/96/10 Eskdalemuir monthly bulletin, October 1996.

WM/ES/96/11 Eskdalemuir monthly bulletin, November 1996.

WM/ES/96/2 Eskdalemuir monthly bulletin, February 1996.

WM/ES/96/3 Eskdalemuir monthly bulletin, March 1996.

WM/ES/96/4 Eskdalemuir monthly bulletin, April 1996.

WM/ES/96/5 Eskdalemuir monthly bulletin, May 1996.

WM/ES/96/6 Eskdalemuir monthly bulletin, June 1996.

WM/ES/96/7 Eskdalemuir monthly bulletin, July 1996.

WM/ES/96/8 Eskdalemuir monthly bulletin, August 1996.

WM/ES/96/9 Eskdalemuir monthly bulletin, September 1996.

WM/HA/95/12 Hartland monthly bulletin - December 1995.

WM/HA/96/1 Hartland monthly bulletin, January 1996.

WM/HA/96/10 Hartland monthly bulletin, October 1996.

WM/HA/96/11 Hartland monthly bulletin, November 1996.

WM/HA/96/2 Hartland monthly bulletin, February 1996.

WM/HA/96/3 Hartland monthly bulletin, March 1996.

WM/HA/96/4 Hartland monthly bulletin, April 1996.

WM/HA/96/5 Hartland monthly bulletin, May 1996

WM/HA/96/6 Hartland monthly bulletin, June 1996.

WM/HA/96/7 Hartland monthly bulletin, July 1996.

WM/HA/96/8 Hartland monthly bulletin, August 1996.

WM/HA/96/9 Hartland monthly bulletin, September 1996.

WM/LE/95/12 Lerwick monthly bulletin — December 1995.

WM/LE/96/1 Lerwick monthly bulletin, January 1996.

WM/LE/96/10 Lerwick monthly bulletin, October 1996.

WM/LE/96/11 Lerwick monthly bulletin, November 1996.

WM/ES/96/2 Lerwick monthly bulletin, February 1996.

WM/LE/96/3 Lerwick monthly bulletin, March 1996.

WM/LE/96/4 Lerwick monthly bulletin, April 1996.

WM/LE/96/5 Lerwick monthly bulletin, May 1996.

WM/LE/96/6 Lerwick monthly bulletin, June 1996.

WM/LE/96/7 Lerwick monthly bulletin, July 1996.

WM/LE/96/8 Lerwick monthly bulletin, August 1996.

WM/LE/96/9 Lerwick monthly bulletin, September 1996.

Engineering Geology

WN/95/15 Methods of testing for swelling and shrinkage of soils.

WN/95/16 Some geological aspects of clay swelling and shrinkage.

WN/95/37 Methods for the recognition of geological weakness zones and other surface discontinuities caused by underground mining in Carboniferous terrain. Final report. Part 1: Text.

WN/95/37 Methods for the recognition of geological weakness zones and other surface discontinuities caused by underground mining in Carboniferous terrain. Final report. Part 2: Figures.

WN/95/42 The engineering geology of the Cirencester area. 1:50 000 geological sheet 235.

WN/96/10 Development of electrical tomographic imaging and inversion techniques for mineral exploration: Synthesis Report.

WN/96/12 Development of electrical tomographic imaging and inversion techniques for mineral exploration: Summary Report.

WN/96/25 Non-contact temperature measurements of the Soufriere Hills volcanic dome, Montserrat, West Indies, using portable infra-red thermometers.

Information and data recources

WO/93/3 Links between map databases systems from different scales.

WO/96/2 The BGS Digital Map Production System. Automatic generation of map keys and marginilia.

WO/96/3 Commentary on a British Geological Survey Computing Archive 1965–1985.

WO/96/5 National grid index to British geological field excursion.

Applied Geochemistry

WP/95/14 Forum of European Geological Surveys (FOREGS). Geochemistry Task Group 1994–1996 Report.

Directorate

WQ/96/1 Science in a market economy.

WQ/96/2 Future options for the British Geological Survey.

WQ/96/3 Social trends and their impact on the coastal zone and adjacent seas.

CONFIDENTIAL AND RESTRICTED REPORTS

The BGS produced many confidential reports, mostly for customers; and restricted reports which were mainly interim, giving results that are likely to be published later.

WORKS PUBLISHED OUTSIDE THE BGS AND REGISTERED IN THE BGS LIBRARY

ADAMS, B. 1995. Groundwater quality monitoring; what exactly is being analysed? 5 pages in *The role of geology and hydrogeology in environmental protection, 150th Anniversary Environmental Geology Symposium.* (Dublin: Geological Survey of Ireland 1995.)

ADAMS, B. 1995. Groundwater protection in Gland and Wales. 7 pages in *The role of geology and hydrogeology in environmental protection, 150th Anniversary Environmental Geology Symposium.* (Dublin: Geological Survey of Ireland 1995.)

ARKAI, P, MERRIMAN, R J, ROBERTS, B, PEACOR, D R, and TOTH, M. 1996. Crystallinity, crystallite size and lattice strain of illite-muscovite and chlorite: comparison of XRD and TEM data for diagenetic to epizonal pelites. *European Journal of Mineralogy,* Vol. 8, 1119–1137.

ARMSTRONG H A, JOHNSON, E W, and SCOTT, R W. 1996. Conodont biostratigraphy of the attenuated Dent Group (upper Ordovician) at Hartley Ground, Broughton in Furness, Cumbria, UK. *Proceedings of the Yorkshire Geological Society,* Vol. 51, 9–21.

ARTHURTON, R S. 1995. Implications of physical environemntal change for coastal zone management. 761–764 in International Conference 'Coastal Change '95'. Bordomer IOC.

ARTHURTON, R S. 1996. Awareness of the physical environment — a foundation for coastal decisions. 1–6 in

Partnership in coastal zone management. TAUSSIK, J, and MITCHELL, J (editors). (Cardigan: Samara Publishing Ltd.)

BALSON, P S. 1996. Holocene coastal evolution evidence from the southern North Sea. 127–130 *in* Land–ocean interaction study (LOIS), community research first annual meeting. BARRETT, R L (compiler). *Plymouth Marine Laboratory, LOIS publication,* No. 106.

BARNES. R P, PHILLIPS, E R, and MERRIMAN R J. 1995. Allochthonous Ordovician basaltic rocks of possible island arc affinity in the Southern Uplands, southwest Scotland. 161–170 *in* Current perspectives in the Appalachian–Caledonian Orogen. STIBBARD, J P, VAN STAAL, C R, and CAWOOD, P A (editors). *Special Paper of the Geological Association of Canada,* No. 41.

BATH, A H, McCARTNEY, R A, RICHARDS, H G, METCALFE, R, and CRAWFORD, M B. 1996. Groundwater chemistry in the Sellafield area. *Quarterly Journal of Engineering Geology,* Vol. 29, S39–S57.

BELL, B R, WILLIAMSON, I T, HEAD, F E, and JOLLEY, D W. 1996. On the origin of a reddened interflow bed within the Palaeocene lava field of north Skye. *Scottish Journal of Geology,* Vol. 32, 117–126.

BENEDITTI, M F, VAN RIEMSJDIK W H, KOOPAL, L K, KINNIBURGH, D G, GOODDY, D C, and MILNE, C J. 1996. Metal ion binding by natural organic matter: from the model to the field. *Geochemica et Cosmochimica Acta,* Vol. 60, 2503–2513.

BLOOMFIELD, J. 1996. Characterisation of hydrogeologically significant fracture distributions in the Chalk: an example from the Upper Chalk of southern England. *Journal of Hydrology,* Vol. 184, 355–380.

BLOOMFIELD, J P, and WILLIAMS, A T. 1995. An empirical liquid permeability–gas permeability correlation for use in aquifer properties studies. *Quarterly Journal of Engineering Geology,* Vol. 28, 143–150.

BLOOMFIELD, J P, BREWERTON, L J, and ALLEN, D J. 1995. Regional trends in matrix porosity and dry density of the Chalk of England. *Quarterly Journal of Engineering Geology,* Vol. 28, 131–142.

BOUCH, J E, HOLE, M J, TREWIN, N H, and MORTON, A C. 1995. Low-temperature aqueous mobility of the rare-earth elements during sandstone diagenesis. *Journal of the Geological Society of London,* Vol. 152, 895–898.

BRANDON, A, RILEY, N J, WILSON, A A, and ELLISON, R A. 1995. New early Namurian marine bands from central and northern England implications for correlation and sequence stratigraphy [Abstract]. Proceedings of the Petroleum Exploration Society of Great Britain Conference. (London: Geological Society.)

BRANDON, A, RILEY, N J, WILSON, A A, and ELLISON, R A. 1995. Three new early Namurian (E_{1c}–E_{2a}) marine bands in central and northern England, UK, and their bearing on correlation with the Askrigg Block. *Proceedings of the Yorkshire Geological Society,* Vol. 50, 333–355.

BREW, D S. 1996. Late Weichselian to early Holocene subaqueous dune formation and burial of the North Sea Northumberland coast. *Marine Geology,* Vol. 134, 203–211.

BREW, D S. 1996. Holocene depositional history of the central Wash. 1996. 126 *in* Land-ocean interaction study (LOIS), community research project first annual meeting. BARRETT, R L (compiler). *Plymouth Marine Laboratory Laboratory, LOIS Publication,* No. 106.

BREW, D S, CIAVOLA, P, MANTOVANI, F, and SIMEONI, U. 1995. Coastal change in Albania — a case study from Kavavasta Lagoon. 473–482 *in* Proceedings, International Conference 'Coastal Change '95'. Bordomer–IOC.

BREW, D S, MITLEHNER, A G, and FUNNELL, B M. 1996. Holocene vegetation and salinity changes in the upper Blyth Estuary, Suffolk. *Bulletin of the Geological Society of Norfolk,* Vol. 43, (1993), 45–61.

BROCKE, R, FATKA, O, MOLYNEUX S G, and SERVAIS, T. 1995. First appearance of selected early Ordovician acritarch taxa from peri-Gondwana. 473–476 *in* 7th International Symposium on the Ordovician System, Ordovician odyssey, short papers. JOHN, D, COOPER, M, DROSER, L, and FINNEY, S C (editors). (Fullerton: Pacific Section Society for Sedimentary Geology.)

BROWNE, M A E, and GRINLY, D. 1996. Clackmannanshire landscape and geology. *Forth Naturalist and Historian,* Vol. 19, 3–26.

CANNING, J C, HENNEY, P J, MORRISON, M A, and GASKARTH, J W. 1996. Geochemistry of late Caledonian minettes from northern Britain: implications for the sub-continental lithospheric mantle. *Mineralogical Magazine,* Vol. 60, 221–236.

CARROLL, S. 1995. Discussion on vitrinite reflectivity and the structure and burial history of the Old Red Sandstone of the Midland Valley. *Journal of the Geological Society of London,* Vol. 152, 567–568.

CHENERY, S R N, WILLIAM, T, ELLIOTT, T A, FOREY P L, and WERDELIN, L. 1996. Determination of rare earth elements in biological and mineral apatite by EPMA and LAMP-ICP-MS. *Mikrochimica Acta* [Suppl.], Vol. 13, 259–269.

CHISHOLM, J I, WATERS, C N, HALLSWORTH, C R, TURNER, N, STRONG, G E, and JONES, N S. 1996. Provenance of Lower Coal Measures around Bradford, West Yorkshire. *Proceedings of the Yorkshire Geological Society,* Vol. 51, 153–165.

COOPER, A H. 1996. Gypsum dissolution geohazards. *Geochemist,* Vol. 6. 18–19.

CORNWELL, J D, KIMBELL, G S, and OGILVY, R D. 1996. Geophysical evidence for basement structure in Suffolk, East Anglia. *Journal of the Geological Society of London,* Vol. 153, 207–211.

CRAMPON, N, CUSTODIO, E, and DOWNING, R A. 1996. The hydrogeology of Western Europe: a basic framework. *Quarterly Journal of Engineering Geology,* Vol. 29, 163–180.

CZERNICHOWSKI–LAURIOL, I, SANJUAN, B, ROCHELLE, C, BATEMAN, K, PEARCE, J, and BLACKWELL, P. 1996. Analysis of the geochemical aspects of the underground disposal of CO_2. 565–583 in *Deep injection disposal of hazardous and industrial waste.* (Academic Press.)

DALY, J S, HEAMAN, L M, FITZGERALD, R C, MENUGE, J F, BREWER, T S, and MORTON, A C. 1995. Age and coastal evolution of crystalline basement in western Iceland and Rockall. 433–434 *in* The petroleum geology of Icelandic offshore basins. CROKER, P F, and SHANNON, P M (editors). *Special Publication of the Geological Society of London,* No. 93.

DARLING, W G, GIZAW, B, and ARUSEI, M K. 1996. Lake–groundwater relationships and fluid–rock interaction in the East African Rift Valley: isotopic evidence. *Journal of African Earth Sciences,* Vol. 22, 423–432.

DENNISS, A M, HARRIS, A J L, CHARLTON, R W, FRANCIS, P W, and ROTHERY, D A. 1996. The 1993 Lascar pyroclastic flow imaged by JERS-1. *International Journal of Remote Sensing,* Vol. 17, 1975–1980.

DE SANTIS, A, and BARRACLOUGH, D R. 1996. A note on two expressions for the spatial power spectrum of the geomagnetic field. *Annali di Geofisica,* Vol. XXXIX, 529–531.

DE SOUZA FILHO, C R, DRURY, S A, DENNISS, A M, CARLTON, R W T, and ROTHERY, D A. 1996. Restoration of corrupted optical Fuyo-1 (JERS-1) data using frequency domain techniques. *Photogrammetric Engineering & Remote Sensing,* Vol. 62, 1037–1047.

EDMUNDS, W M. 1996. Bromine geochemistry of British groundwaters. *Mineralogical Magazine,* Vol. 60, 275–284.

EDMUNDS, W M. 1996. Geochemical framework for water quality studies in sub-Saharan Africa. *Journal of African Earth Sciences,* Vol. 22, 385–389.

EDMUNDS, W M. 1996. Indicators in the groundwater environment of rapid environmental change. 135–150 in *Geoindicators, assessing rapid environmental changes in earth systems.* BERGER, A R, and IAMS, W J (editors). (Rotterdam: A A Balkema.)

EDMUNDS, W M, and SMEDLEY, P L. 1996. Groundwater geochemistry and health: an overview. 91–105 in Environmental geochemistry and health. APPLETON, J D, FUGE, R, and MCCALL, G J H (editors). *Special Publication of the Geological Society of London,* No. 113.

EDMUNDS, W M, and KEY, R M. 1996. Hydrogeochemistry as an aid to geological interpretation: the Glen Roy area, Scotland. *Journal of the Geological Society of London,* Vol. 153, 839–852.

ELLISON, R A, ALI, J R, HINE, N M, and JOLLEY, D W. 1996. Recognition of Chron C25n in the upper Paleocene Upnor Formation of the London Basin, UK. 185–193 in *Correlation of the Early Paleogene in Northwest Europe. Special Publication of the Geological Society of London,* No. 101.

EMELEUS, C H, ALLWRIGHT, E A, KERR, A C, and WILLIAMSON, I T. 1996. Red tuffs in the Palaeocene lava successions of the Inner Hebrides. *Scottish Journal of Geology,* Vol. 32, 83–89.

EVANS, D. 1996. The BGS deep-tow boomer meeets the Storegga Slide. *Edinburgh Geologist,* Vol. 28, 24–29.

EVANS, D, KING, E L, KENYON, N H, BRETT, C, and WALLIS, D. 1996. Evidence for long-term instability in the Storegga Slide region off western Norway. *Marine Geology,* Vol. 130, 281–292.

EVANS, R. 1996. Exploring the volcanic margins: alternatives to seismic reflection profiling. Abstract, 3rd UK Atlantic Margin Conference Aberdeen. Robert Gordon University Offshore Management Centre.

FENSOME, R A, RIDING, J B, and TAYLOR, F J R. 1996. Dinoflagellates. 107–169 in *Palynology: principles and applications.* JANSONIUS, J, and MCGREGOR, D C (editors). (American Association of Stratigraphic Palynologists Foundation.)

FLINN, D, KEY, R M, and KHOO, T T. 1996. The chloritoid schists of Shetland and their thermal metamorphism. *Scottish Journal of Geology,* Vol. 32, 67–82.

FLOYD, J D. 1996. Lithostratigraphy of the Ordovician rocks in the Southern Uplands: Crawford Group, Moffat Shale Group, Leadhills Supergroup. *Transactions of the Royal Society of Edinburgh: Earth Sciences,* Vol. 86, 153–165.

FORDYCE, F M, MASARA, D, and APPLETON, J D. 1996. Stream sediment, soil and forage chemistry as indicators of cattle mineral status in northeast Zimbabwe. 23–37 in Environmental geochemistry and health. APPLETON, J D, FUGE, R, and MCCALL, G J H (editors). *Special Publication of the Geological Society of London,* No. 113.

FORSTER, A C, and FORSTER, S C. 1996. Troglodyte dwellings of the Loire Valley, France. *Quarterly Journal of Engineering Geology,* Vol 29, 193–197.

FORSTER, A, JACKSON, P D, and XIANZHONG LI. 1996. Ground motion amplification: an example from the city of Tangshan, China. *Quarterly Journal of Engineering Geology,* Vol 29, 97–101.

FORTEY, N J, MERRIMAN, R J, and HUFF, W D. 1996. Silurian and late Ordovician K-bentonites as a record of late Caledonian volcanism in the British Isles. *Transactions of the Royal Society of Edinburgh: Earth Sciences,* Vol. 86, 167–180.

GAYE, C B, and EDMUNDS, W M. 1996. Groundwater recharge estimation using chloride, stable isotopes and tritium profiles in the sands of northwestern Senegal. *Environmental Geology,* Vol. 27, 246–251.

GLOVER, B W, and MCKIE, T. 1996. A sequence stratigraphical approach to the understanding of basin history in orogenic Neoproterozoic successions: an example from the central Highlands of Scotland. 257–269 in Sequence stratigraphy in British geology. HESSELBO, S P, and PARKINSON, D N (editors). *Special Publication of the Geological Society of London,* No. 103, 257–269.

GLOVER, B W, and PHILPOTT, K. 1995. The Second European Coal Conference. *Geoscientist,* Vol. 5, No. 5, 17–19.

GLOVER, B W, and POWELL, J H. 1996. Interaction of climate and tectonics upon alluvial architecture: Late Carboniferous–Early Permian sequences at the southern margin of the Pennine basin. *Palaeogeography, Palaeoclimatology, Palaeoecology,* Vol. 121, 13–34.

GLOVER, B W, LENG, M J, and CHISHOLM, J I. 1996. A second major fluvial sourceland for the Silesian Pennine Basin of northern England. *Journal of the Geological Society of London,* Vol. 153, 901–906.

GOODDY, D C, SHAND, P, KINNIBURGH, D G, and VAN RIEMSDIJK, W H. 1995. Field-based partition coefficients for trace element in soil solutions. *European Journal of Soil Science,* Vol. 46, 265–285.

GOWING, C J B, and AULT, L. 1996. Field sampling and analytical variations during ICP-AES analysis of stream waters from Wales and the West Midlands. *Spectroscopy Europe,* Vol. 8, 20–26.

GREENBAUM, D, MCDONALD, A J W, and MARSH, S H. 1996. Rapid methods of landslide hazard mapping. Abstract, 11th Thematic Conference and Workshops on Applied Geologic Remote Sensing, Las Vegas.

GUION, P G, JONES, N S, FULTON, I M, and ASHTON, A J. 1995. Effects of a Westphalian channel on coal-seam geometry: a re-appraisal of the 'Dumb Fault' of north Derbyshire. *Proceedings of the Yorkshire Geological Society,* Vol. 50, 317–332.

GUNN, A G, STYLES, M T, ROLLIN, K E, and STEPHENSON, D. 1996. The geology of the Succoth–Brown Hill mafic– ultramafic intrusive complex, near Huntly, Aberdeenshire. *Scottish Journal of Geology,* Vol. 32, 33–49.

HAMLIN, R J O, and MOORLOCK, B S P. 1995. The Kesgrave and Bytham sands and gravels of eastern Suffolk. *Quaternary Newsletter,* No. 77, 17–41.

HARRISON, D J. 1996. Evaluation of limestone deposits for multipurpose applications. 50–68 in International Symposium on Limestone, Subang Jaya, Malaysia, School of Materials and Mineral Resources Engineering, University of Malaysia and Institute of Quarrying.

HARRISON, D J. 1996. Resource management of marine sand and gravel: a European perspective. 15–20 in *Partnership in coastal zone management.* TAUSSIK, J, and MITCHELL J (editors). (Cardigan: Samara Publishing Ltd.)

HIGGO, J J W, NIELSEN, P H, BANNON, M P, HARRISON, I, and CHRISTENSEN, T H. 1996. Effect of geochemical conditions on fate of organic compounds in groundwater. *Environmental Geology,* Vol. 27, 335–346.

HOOKER P J. 1996. An overview of the British Natural Analogue Programme. 109–113 in *6th EC Natural Analogue Working Group Meeting, Santa Fe, New Mexico, USA.* VON MARAVIC, H, and SMELLIE, J (editors). (Luxembourg: European Commission.)

HOOKER, P J, MCBRIDGE, D, and BROWN, M J. 1996. An integrated geoscientific assessment of Wolverhampton. 37–44 in *4th International Conference on Re-Use of Contaminated Land and Landfills, polluted and marginal land.* FORDE, M C (editor). (Edinburgh: Engineering Technics Press.)

HUDSON, J A, LIU, E, and CRAMPIN, S. 1996. The mechanical properties of materials with interconnected cracks and pores. *Geophysical Journal International,* Vol. 124, 105–112.

HUDSON, J A, LIU, E, and CRAMPIN, S. 1996. Transmission properties of a plane fault. *Geophysical Journal International,* Vol. 125, 559–566.

HURST, A, and MILODOWSKI, A. 1996. Thorium distribution in some North Sea sandstones: implications for petrophysical evaluation. *Petroleum Geoscience,* Vol. 2, 59–68.

IXER, R A, YOUNG, B, and STANLEY, C J. 1996. Bismuth-bearing assemblages from the Northern Pennine Orefield. *Mineralogical Magazine,* Vol. 60, 317–324.

JOHNSON, E W, BRIGGS, D E G, and WRIGHT, J L. 1996. Lake District pioneers — the earliest footprints on land. *Geology Today,* Vol. 12, 147–151.

JONES, D G, ROBERTS, P, DE MEIJER, R and STAPEL, K. 1995. Marine and coastal heavy mineral placers: the role of radiometric techniques in exploration, assessment and process control. Abstract, Proceedings of 26th Annual Underwater Mining Institute, Newfoundland.

KARNASSOPOULOU, A, PEARCE, R G, and BOOTH, D C. 1996. A method to determine microearthquake focal mechanisms in the presence of seismic anisotropy. *Tectonophysics,* 261, 115–126.

KELLY, J, THORNTON, I, and SIMPSON, P R. 1996. 1996. Urban geochemistry: a study of the influence of anthropogenic activity on the heavy metal content of soils in traditionally industrial and non-industrial areas of Britain. *Applied Geochemistry,* Vol. 11, 363–370.

KINNIBURGH, D G, and TRAFFORD, J M. 1996. Unsaturated zone pore water chemistry and the edge effect in a beech forest in southern England. *Water, air and soil pollution,* Vol. 92, 421–450.

KINNIBURGH, D G, MILNE, C J, BENEDETTI, M F, PINHEIRO, J P, FILIUS, J, KOOPAL, L K, and VAN RIEMSDIJK, W H. 1996. Metal ion binding by humic acid: application of the NICA-Donnan model. *Environmental Science and Technology,* Vol. 30, 1687–1698.

KLOPPMANN, W, DEVER, L, and EDMUNDS, W M. 1996. Zones d'oxydo-reduction dans l'aquifere de la Craie des bassins de Paris et de l'Allemagne du nord. *Hydrological Sciences Journal,* Vol. 41, 311–326.

LAWRENCE, A R, and CHENERY, C. 1996. Urban groundwater. 61–80 in *Urban geoscience.* MCCALL, G J, DE MULDER, E F J, and MARKER, B R (editors). (Rotterdam: A A Balkema.)

LAWRENCE, A R, STUART, M E, BARKER, J A, and TESTER, D J. 1996. Contamination of Chalk groundwater by chlorinated solvents: a case study of deep penetration by non-aqueous phase liquids. *Water and Environmental Management,* Vol. 10, 263–272.

LAXTON, J L, and BECKEN, K. 1996. The design and implementation of a spatial database for the production of geological maps. *Computers and Geosciences,* Vol. 22, 723–733.

LEWIS, P M. 1995. A new type of map for coastal planning. 24–29 in *Irish Sea Forum, coastal zone planning seminar report.* (Preston: County Offices.)

LEWIS, P M. 1995. Presentation of geoscientific data in the coastal zone. 379–387 in *International Symposium on GIS and computer mapping for coastal zone management.* (Cork: Coastal Resources Centre.)

LUCEK, E A, and CLARK, T D G. 1996. The use of interplanetary scintillation maps in the prediction of geomagnetic activity. *Annales Geophysicae,* Vol. 14, 131–136.

LUCEK, E A, CLARK, T D G, and MOORE, V. 1996. The use of various interplanetary scintillation indices within geomagnetic forecasts. *Annales Geophysicae,* Vol. 14, 139–148.

MACMILLAN, S. 1996. A geomagnetic jerk for the early 1990s. *Earth and Planetary Science Letters,* Vol. 137, 189–192.

MARSH, S H, and GREALLY, K. 1996. From TM to JERS-1 to ASTER: toward mineral identification with satellite data. Abstract: 11th Thematic Conference and Workshops on Applied Geologic Remote Sensing, Las Vegas.

MATHERS, S J, and ZALASIEWICZ, J. 1996. A gravel beach-rip channel system: the Westleton Beds (Pleistocene) of Suffolk, England. *Proceedings of the Geologists' Association,* Vol. 107, 57–67.

MCADAM, D. 1995. Arthur's Seat. p.9 in World Mountain Running Trophy. (Edinburgh District Council.)

MCCOURT, W J, CROW, M J, COBBING, E J, and AMIN, T C. 1996. Mesozoic and Cenozoic plutonic evolution of SE Asia: evidence from Sumatra, Indonesia. 321–335 in Tectonic evolution of Southeast Asia. HALL, R, and BLUNDELL, D (editors). *Special Publication of the Geological Society of London,* No. 106.

MCKENNA, G, and ROBINSON, E. 1996. Geological photographs: historical magic or national record? *Geology Today,* Vol. 12, 114–116.

MCLEAN, D, and CHISHOLM, J I. 1996. Reworked palynomorphs as provenance indicators in the Yeadonian of the Pennine Basin. *Proceedings of the Yorkshire Geological Society,* Vol 51, 141–152.

MERRIMAN, R J, and KEMP, S J. 1996. Clay minerals and sedimentary basin maturity. *Mineralogical Society Bulletin,* No. 111, 7–8.

MITCHELL, C, and WOOSNAM, R. 1995. Novel processing of flake graphite. In *Processing for profit.* (Amsterdam: Industrial Minerals.)

MOLYNEUX, S G, LE HERISSE, A, and WICANDER, R. 1996. Paleozoic phytoplankton. 493–529 in P*alynology, principles and applications.* JANSONIUS, J, and MACGREGOR, D C (editors). (American Association of Stratigraphic Palynologists Foundation.)

MORTON, A C, CLAQUE-LONG, J C, and BERGE, C. 1996. SHRIMP constraints on sediment provenance and transport history on the Mesozoic Statfjord Formation, North Sea. *Journal of the Geological Society of London,* Vol. 153, 915–930.

MUSSON, R M W. 1996. The seismicity of the British Isles. *Annali di Geofisica,* Vol. XXXIX, 463–469.

MUSSON, R M W. 1995. Historical seismicity of south China from European sources — example of the Hong Kong newspaper press. *Acta Seismologica Sinica,* Vol. 17, 393–395.

NOBLE, S R, HYSLOP, E K, and HIGHTON, A J. 1996. High-precision U-Pb monazite geochronology of the c. 806 Ma Grampian Shear Zone and the implications for the evolution of the Central Highlands of Scotland. *Journal of the Geological Society of London,* Vol. 153, 511–514.

NORTHMORE, K J, BELL, F G, and CULSHAW, M G. 1996. The engineering properties and behaviour of the brickearth of south Essex. *Quarterly Journal of Engineering Geology,* Vol. 29, 147–161.

OLDROYD, D R, and MCKENNA, G. 1995. A note on Andrew Ramsay's unpublished report on the St David's area, recently discovered: notes and correspondence. *Annals of Science,* Vol. 52, 193–196.

OVADIA, D C. 1996. Geological information and 3D GIS. European Commission Joint Research Centre, Draft proceedings of the 2nd EC-GIS Workshop.

OVADIA, D C. 1996. KISC — Keep it simple and cheap: a policy for reducing the cost base of computing in a geological survey without risking its efficacy. P 800 in *International Consortium of Geological Surveys for Earth Computer Sciences proceedings.* TROELSTRUP, S (editor). (Geological Survey of Denmark and Greenland.)

OVADIA, D C. 1996. Report to ICGSECS-10 from the British Geological Survey for the period May 1994 to May 1995. 71–73 in International Consortium of Geological Surveys for Earth Computer Sciences, Copenhagen.

TROELSTRUP, S (editor). (Geological Survey of Denmark and Greenland.)

OWENS, B. 1996. Paleozoic spores and pollen: Upper Carboniferous spores and pollen. 597–606 in *Palynology, principles and applications.* JANSONIUS, J, and MCGREGOR, D C (editors). (American Association of Stratigraphic Palynogists Foundation.)

PALLIANI, R B, RIDING, J B, and TORRICELLI, S. 1996. *Polygonium jurassicum sp.* nov., a polygonomorph acritarch from the lower Toarcian (lower Jurassic) of the Tethyan realm. *Palynology,* Vol. 20, 157–161.

PEARCE, J M, HOLLOWAY, S, WACKER, H, NEILS, M K, ROCHELLE, C, AND BATEMAN. 1996. Natural occurences as analogues for the geological disposal of carbon dioxide. *Energy Conversion Management,* Vol. 37, 1123–1128.

PENN, I E. 1996. Geoscience training in today's British Geological Survey. 625–632 in Geoscience education and training, in schools and universitites, for industry and public awareness. DORRIK, A V, STOW, and MCCALL, G J H (editors). (Rotterdam A A: Balkema.)

PETTERSON, M G, and WINDLEY, B F, and SULLIVAN, M. 1995. A petrological, chronological, structural and geochemical review of Kolistan batholith and its relationship to regional tectonics. 47–70 in *Geology and geodynamic evolution of the Himalayan Collision Zone.* SHARMA , K K (editor). (Oxford: Pergamon Press.)

PHILLIPS, E R, and MAY, F. 1996. The Glas Bheinn Appinitic Complex, Glen Roy: a model for foliation development during emplacement. *Scottish Journal of Geology,* Vol. 32, 9–21.

PHILLIPS, E R, BARNES, R P, MERRIMAN, R J, and FLOYD, J D. 1995. The tectonic significance of Ordovician basin igneous rock in the Southern Uplands, southwest Scotland. *Geological Magazine,* Vol. 132, 549–556.

PLAG, H P, WINGFIELD, R T R and 10 others. 1996. Late Quaternary relative sea-level changes and the role of glaciation upon continental shelves. *Terra Nova,* Vol. 8, 213–222.

POITRASSON, F, CHENERY, S, OELKERS, E H, and BLAND, D J. 1996. Sur les méchanismes d'alteration contrastes de la monazite et leurs conséquences. P101 in *Reunion des sciences de la terre 16ème, Orleans; Dynamique et economie de la terre.* (Paris: Société Géologique de France.)

REES, J G, CORNWELL, J D, DABEK, Z K, and MERRIMAN, R J. 1996. The Apedale Tuffs, North Staffordshire: probable remnants of a late Asbian/Brigantian (P1a) volcanic centre. 345–357 in Recent advances in Lower Carboniferous geology. STROGEN, P, SOMERVILLE, I D, and JONES, G L (editors). *Special Publication of the Geological Society of London,* No. 107.

RICHARDS, P C. 1995. A vast untapped potential. *World energy yearbook; 1995,* 117–118.

RICHARDS, P C, GATLIFF, R W, QUINN, M F, and FANNIN, N G T. 1996. Petroleum potential of the Falkland Islands offshore area chards. *Journal of Petroleum Geology,* Vol. 19, 161–182.

RICHARDS, P C, GATLIFF, R W, QUINN, M F, WILLIAMSON, J P, and FANNIN, N G T. 1996. The geological evolution of the Falkland Islands continental shelf. 105–128 in Weddell Sea tectonics and Gondwana Break-up. STOREY, B C, KING, E C, and LIVERMORE, R A (editors). *special publication of the Geological Society of London,* No. 108.

RIDDLER, G J H. 1995. Towards an international classification of reserves and resources. *In* Joint Seminar for the Non-Ferrous Industry. Euromataux.

RIDING, J B, and ILYINA, V I. 1996. *Protobatioladinium elatmaensis* sp.nov., a dinoflagellate cyst from the Bathonain of Russia. *Journal of Micropalaeontology,* Vol. 152, 150.

RIDING, J B, and IOANNIDES, N S. 1996. A review of Jurassic dinoflagellate cyst biostratigraphy and global provincialism. *Bulletin de la Société Géologique de France,* Vol. 167, 3–14.

RILEY, N J and OWENS, B. 1996. The Mansfield Marine Band: a case study in scientific conservation and industrial co-operation. 707–714 in *Geoscience education and training, in schools and universities for industry and public awarebess.* STOW, D A V, and MCCALL, G J H (editors). (Rotterdam: A A Balkema.)

RIPPON J, READ, W A, and PARK, R G. 1996. The Ochil Faults and the Kincardine basin: key structures in the tectonic evolution of the Midland Valley of Scotland. *Journal of the Geological Society of London,* Vol. 153, 573–587.

ROBERTS, B, MERRIMAN, R J, HIRONS, S R, FLETCHER, C J N, and WILSON, D. 1996. Synchronous very low-grade metamorphism, contraction and inversion in the central part of the Welsh Lower Palaeozoic Basin. *Journal of the Geological Society of London,* Vol. 153, 277–285.

ROBINS, N S. 1996. Hydrogeological characteristics of the Celtic upland terrains of Great Britain and Northern Ireland: *Uisqebaugh* versus *Loch a Phuill.* 65–71 in *Hydrologie dans les pays celtiques. Les Colloques,* No. 79. (Paris: INRA.)

ROBINS, N S, and YOUNGER, P L. 1996. Coal abandonment — mine water in surface and near-surface environment: some historical evidence from the United Kingdom. 253–262 in *Minerals, Metals and the Environment II Conference; Prague.* (Institution of Mining and Metallurgy.)

ROSE, J, GULAMALI, N, MOORLOCK, B S P, HAMBLIN, R J O, JEFFERY, D H, ANDERSON, E, LEE, J A, and RIDING, J B. 1995. Pre-glacial and glacial Quaternary sediments, How Hill near Ludham, Norfolk, England. *Bulletin of the Geological Society of Norfolk,* Vol. 45, 3–28.

RUSHTON, A W A, and HUGHES, N C. 1996. Biometry, systematics and biogeography of the late Cambrian trilobite *Maladioidella abdita. Transactions of the Royal Society of Edinburgh: Earth Sciences,* Vol. 86, 247–256.

RUSHTON, A W A, STONE, P, and HUGHES, R A. 1996. Biostratigraphical control of thrust models for the Southern Uplands of Scotland. *Transactions of the Royal Society of Edinburgh: Earth Sciences,* Vol. 86, 137–151.

RUSHTON, A W A, TUNNICLIFF, S P, and TRIPP, R P. 1996. The faunas of the Albany Group in the Girvan area, and their palaeogeographical implications. *Scottish Journal of Geology,* Vol. 32, 23–32.

SHAW, M H, and GUNN, A G. 1995. PGE exploration on the alkaline intrusions of north-west Scotland. In *Prospectors and Developers Association of Canada Annual Convention.*

SHAW, R P. 1995. Long Rake Spar Mine, Youlgreave. *Bulletin of the Peak District Mines Historical Society,* Vol. 12, No. 5, 35–37.

SIMPSON, P R, BREWARD, N, FLIGHT, D M A, and LISTER, R. 1996. High resolution regional hydrogeochemical baseline mapping of stream water of Wales, the Welsh borders and west Midlands region. *Applied Geochemistry,* Vol. 11, 621–623.

SKLASH, M G, BEVEN, K J, GILMAN, K, and DARLING, W G. 1996. Isotope studies of pipeflow at Plynlimon, Wales, UK. *Hydrological Processes,* Vol. 10, 921–944.

SMEDLEY, P L. 1996. Arsenic in rural groundwater in Ghana. *Journal of African Earth Science*s, Vol. 22, 459–470.

SMEDLEY, P L, EDMUNDS, W M, and PELIG-BA, K B. 1996. Mobility of arsenic in groundwater in the Obuasi gold-mining area of Ghana: some implications for human health. 163–181 in Environmental geochemistry and health. APPLETON, J D, FUGE, R, and MCCALL, G J H (editors). *Special Publication of the Geological Society of London*, No. 113.

SMITH, A, and ELLISON, R A. 1996. Recent mapping of the Lower Thames terraces by the British Geological Survey. 65–69 in *The Quaternary of the lower reaches of the Thames, field guide*. BRIDGLAND, D R, ALLEN, P, and HAGGART, B A (editors). (Durham: Quaternary Research Association.)

SMITH, B, POWELL, J H, BRADLEY, A D, GEDEON, R, and AMRO, H. 1995. Naturally occurring uranium pollution in Jordan. *Mining Environmental Magazine*, March, 7–10.

SMITH, R A. 1995. The Siluro-Devonian evolution of the southern Midland Valley of Scotland. *Geological Magazine*, Vol. 132, 503–513.

SOUZA FILHO, C R DE, DRURY, S A, DENNISS, A M, CARLTON, R W T, and ROTHERY, D A. 1996. Restoration of Corrupted Optical Fuyo-1 (JERS-1) Data using Frequency Domain Techniques. *Photogrammetric Engineering & Remote Sensing*, Vol. 62, 1037–1047.

STOVER, L E H, RIDING, J B, and 9 others. 1996. Mesozoic–Tertiary dinoflagellates, acritarchs and prasinophytes. 641–750 in *Palynology, principles and applications*. JANSONIUS, J, and MCGREGOR, D C (editors). *American Association of Stratigraphic Palynologists Foundation*.

STROES-GASCOYNE, S, and WEST, J M. 1996. An overview of microbial research related to high-level nuclear waste disposal with emphasis on the Canadian concept for the disposal of nuclear fuel waste. *Canadian Journal of Microbiology*, Vol. 42, 349–366.

SUMBLER, M G, and BARRON, A J M. 1996. Day excursion to the Cotswolds. *Mercian Geologist*, Vol. 14, 34–37.

SUMBLER, M G, and IVIMEY-COOK, H C. 1996. Temporary sections in the Jurassic strata near Leadenham, Lincolnshire. *Mercian Geologist*, Vol. 14, 4–11.

TALBOT, D K, BALL, T K, and JONES, D G. 1996. The use of geoscience datasets for mapping risk posed by natural radioactivity. Abstract, Regional Geochemistry Workshop on environmental and legislative uses of regional geochemical baseline data for sustainable development. BGS Minerals Industry Forum.

TAYLOR, B J. 1996. Taxed to capacity: the role of the Briitsh Geological Survey, then and now. 737–745 in *Geoscience education and training, in schools and universities, for industry and public awareness*. STOW, D A V, and MCCALL, G J H (editors). (Rotterdam: A A Balkema.)

TAYLOR, B J, and SUTTON, I D. 1996. The public understanding of geoscience: introduction. 635–646 in *Geoscience education and training, in schools and universities, for industry and public awareness*. STOW, D A V, and MCCALL, G J H (editors). (Rotterdam: A A Balkema.)

THOMAS, J E. 1996. The occurrence of the dinoflagellate cyst Apectodinium (Costa & Downie 1976) Lentin & Williams 1977 in the Moray and Montrose Groups (Danian to Thanetian) of the UK central North Sea. 115–120 in Correlation of the Early Paleogene in Northwest Europe. KNOX, R W O'B, CORFIELD, R M, and DUNAY, R E (editors). *Special Publication of the Geological Society of London*, No. 101.

THOMSON, A W P. 1996. Non-linear predictions of Ap by activity class and numerical value. *PAGEOPH*, Vol. 146, 163–193.

THOMSON, A W P. 1996. A statistical relationship between coronal hole central meridian passage and geomagnetic activity. *Journal of Geomagnetism and Geoelectricity*, Vol. 47, 1263–1275.

WALLIS, D G. 1996. Remote control of a deep ocean rock drill. 291–300 in *Subsea control and data acquisition*. ADRIAANSEN, L, PHILLIPS, R, REES, C, and CATTANACH, J (editors). (London: Mechanical Engineering Publications.)

WARRINGTON, G. 1996. British Triassic palaeontology: supplement 20. *Albertiana*, No. 17, 65–66.

WARRINGTON, G. 1996. Mesozoic–Tertiary spores and pollen: Triassic spores and pollen. 755–766 in *Palynology, principles and applications*. JANSONIUS, J, and MCGREGOR, D C (editors). (American Association of Stratigraphic Palynologists Foundation.)

WARRINGTON, G. 1996. Mineralisation at Alderley Edge, Cheshire. *British Micromount Society Newsletter*, Vol. 45, 9–10.

WARRINGTON, G. 1996. Palaeozoic spores and pollen: Permian spores and pollen. 607–619 in *Palynology, principles and applications*. JANSONIUS, J, and MCGREGOR, D C (editors). (American Association of Stratigraphic Palynologists Foundation.)

WATERS, C N, AITKENHEAD, N, JONES, N S, and CHISHOLM, J I. 1996. Late Carboniferous stratigraphy and sedimentology of the Bradford area, and its implications for the regional geology of northern England. *Proceedings of the Yorkshire Geological Society*, Vol. 51, 87–102.

WATERS, C N, MAYNARD, J R, and WIGNALL, P B. 1996. New developments in the Late Carboniferous geology of the central Pennines, northern England: a review. *Proceedings of the Yorkshire Geological Society* , Vol. 51, 81–86.

WEST, J M, and MCKINLEY, I. 1996. Some bugs like it hot. *New Scientist*, Vol. 152, 42–45.

WEST, J M, SMEDLEY, P L, and PAINTSIL, A. 1996. Arsenic in drinking waters in the Obuasi area, Ghana — the role of microbiology. 699–702 in 4th International Symposium on the Geochemistry of the Earth's Surface, Ilkley, Yorkshire. University of Leeds.

WESTHEAD, R K, and MATHER, A E. 1996. An updated lithostratigraphy for the Purbeck Limestone Group in the Dorset type-area. *Proceedings of the Geologists' Association*, Vol. 107, 117–128.

WHITE, R S, and MORTON, A C. 1995. The Iceland plume and its influence on the evolution of the NE Atlantic. *Journal of the Geological Society of London*, Vol. 152, 933.

WILKINSON, I P. 1996. Geological controls governing Anglo-Saxon settlement in Framland Wapentake, north-eastern Leicestershire. 53–82 in *Anglo-Saxon landscapes in the East Midlands*. BOURNE, J (editor). (Leicester: Museums, Arts & Records Service.)

WILLIAMS, G M. 1996. The UK research base for reliable application of intrinsic remediation. Abstract, IBC conference on Intrinsic Bioremediation.

WILLIAMS, M, and SIVETER, D J. 1996. Lithofacies-influenced ostracod associations in the middle Ordovician Bromide Formation, Oklahoma, USA. *Journal of Micropalaeontology*, Vol. 15, 69–81.

WOODCOCK, N H, BUTLER, A J, DAVIES, J R, and WATERS, R A. 1996. Sequence stratigraphical analysis of late Ordovician and early Siluruian depositional systems in the Welsh Basin: a critical assessment. 197–207 in Sequence stratigraphy in British geology. HESSELBO, S P, and PARKINSON, D N (editors). *Geological Society of London Special Publication*, No. 103.

WOODS, M A, and JONES, N S. 1996. The sedimentology and biostratigraphy of a temporary exposure of Blackdown Greensand (Lower Cretaceous, Upper Albian) at Blackborough, Devon. *Proceedings of the Ussher Society*, Vol. 9, 37–40.

XIANGUANG, H, SIVETER, D J, WILLIAMS, M, WALOSSEK, D, and BERGSTROM, J. 1996. Appendages of the arthropod *Kunmingella* from the early Cambrian of China: its bearing on the systematic position of the Bradoriida and the fossil record of the Ostracoda. *Philosophical Transactions of the Royal Society of London*, Vol. 351, 1131–1145.

YOUNG, S R. 1996. Summary of eruptive events and monitoring procedures at Soufriere Hills volcano, Montserrat, West Indies, 18 July 1995 to June 1996. *IAVCEI News*, Vol. 1, 2–4.

ZENG, X A, and MACBETH, C. 1996. A case example of near-surface correction for multicomponent VSPS. *Geophysical Prospecting*, Vol. 44, 889–910.

Appendix 4　Staff List, March 1997†

Central Directorate

Keyworth

Director		Dr P J Cook *FGS CGeol*
SPSec	7(A)	Mrs S A McIlfatrick

Secretary (Grd 6)

	3(S)	D Hackett
PSec	8(A)	Mrs J A Drury

Central Directorate Support Group

Grd 7	4(S)	Dr A S Howard
SSO	5(S)	Dr D E Bailey
		Dr N Turner
HSO	6(S)	D G Bate
Ty	9(A)	Mrs W J Crosby

Personnel

Personnel Officer (SEO)

	5(A)	J Orr

PERSONNEL

HEO	6(A)	Mrs M A Squires
EO	7(A)	Mrs J M Cutler★
		W Robinson
		Mrs S A White✳
AO	8(A)	A L Crosby
		Mrs K G Smith
		Mrs S Stocks
		J Wraith
AA	9(A)	Mrs P Gil-Bennett

Facilities Management

Keyworth

SPTO	5(T)	G S Bowick *MBIFM MCIBSE CEng*
HEO	6(A)	A P Cooke
HPTO	6(T)	P C Gray
		L H Wright
EO	7(A)	Miss S E Nunn
PTO	7(T)	D A Gubb
		G M Shenton
AO	8(A)	Mrs B Hadley
		M A Nice
		vacancy
Ty	9(A)	Mrs M A Glover
		Mrs S M Gibson
SGB1	8(T)	Mrs B Hanley
		Mrs P A Newham¶
		Mrs G S Spencer¶
SGB2	9(T)	G Goode
		J R Kirk
		J Stocker
StO	8(T)	M Spencer *CIPS*
Tec 2	9(T)	A J Adkin
		D R Bowman
		J T Glover
		R Mills
		G L Minkley
		F Staples
		G S Upton
		H C Wallis
		R M Wilkinson
		vacancy
SG	9(T)	Mrs S Cartwright¶
		B A Cohen
		W R Davison
		J D Fenton

		R D Holbrook
		D Huscroft
		C Jordan
		A M Spencer
		vacancy

Murchison House

HPTO	6(T)	*vacancy*
Tec 2	9(T)	M D C Laird
SG	9(T)	C A Bunyan
		W C Trench
AO	8(A)	G Hartley

Finance and Accounts

Keyworth

Finance Officer (SEO)

	5(A)	Mrs E B Walton

Programmes and Commercial

HEO	6(A)	A P Cox
EO	7(A)	D R Adam
		Mrs V M Antcliff
		A C Connet
		Miss L K Riley
		Ms J Wright
AO	8(A)	Mrs R A Pharoah¶

Accounts and Operations

HEO	6(A)	Mrs C A Elliott
EO	7(A)	Mrs D R Matheson
AO	8(A)	Miss D R Bagshaw
		R D Crosby
		Mrs L Glew
		G D Jackson✳
		Miss G M Kovac
		Mrs J G Yarwood★
		vacancy
AA(c)	9(C)	Mrs S L Carr

Budgets

HEO	6(A)	Mrs C V Golder
EO	7(A)	Miss T J Henson
		Mrs A J Loveland
AO	8(A)	Mrs K Kennedy

Contracts

HEO	6(A)	P Cottis
EO	7(A)	S D Jackson
AO	8(A)	Miss S S Reveley

Local Administration

Murchison House

HEO	6(A)	K A Tait
EO	7(A)	Miss F A Jackson
		J G Kerr
		Mrs J F Pringle-Stewart
AO	8(A)	Mrs E C Abrahams¶
		Mrs J Broughton¶✳
		B M Connon
		I P Davies
		Mrs M S C Mackie¶
		Mrs C S O'Brien¶
		Miss N G Owenson
AA	9(A)	Mrs S MacIver
Ty	9(A)	Mrs S M Greig¶
		Miss K A Fergusson
SGB1	9(T)	Mrs J Ormiston¶
		vacancy
SGB2	9(T)	J Glendinning¶

THEMATIC MAPS AND ONSHORE SURVEYS

The onshore mapping programme of the United Kingdom; the collection, interpretation and exploitation of regional onshore geophysical data; and the maintenance of related geological and geophysical databases.

Keyworth

Assistant Director (Grd 5)

	2(S)	Dr P M Allen *FGS CGeol*
PSec	8(A)	Miss L J Oxby

Highlands and Islands

Murchison House

Group Manager (Grd 6)

	3(S)	Dr D I J Mallick *FGS CGel*
PSec	8(A)	Mrs M W Kinnear¶
Grd 7	4(S)	Dr D Gould *FGS CGeol*
		MIMM
		Dr J R Mendum
		J W Merritt
		Dr M Smith *FGS CGeol*
		Dr D Stephenson
SSO	5(S)	C A Auton *FGS CGeol*
		Dr A J Highton *FGS CGeol*
		Dr S Robertson
		C W Thomas *FGS CGeol*
SO	7(S)	Miss J E Cavill

Overseas

Grd 7	4(S)	Dr R M Key
		Dr M G Petterson

Scottish Lowlands and Northern England

Murchison House

Group Manager (Grd 6)

	3(S)	Dr D J Fettes *FGS CGeol*
PSec	8(A)	Mrs L B Gray
Grd 7	4(S)	A M Aitken *FGS CGeol*
		Dr R P Barnes
		M A E Browne *FGS CGeol*
		I B Cameron
		Dr J D Floyd *FGS CGeol*
		Mr D J D Lawrence
		A D McAdam *FGS CGeol*
		A A McMillan *FGS CGeol*
		Dr D Millward *FGS CGeol*
		Dr S K Monro *FGS CGeol*
		Dr P Stone *FGS CGeol*
		Dr D G Woodhall *FGS CGeol*
		B Young *FGS CGeol FIMM CEng*

SSO	5(S)	Dr M C Akhurst
		H F Barron *FGS*
		M T Dean
		D N Halley
		Dr E W Johnson *FGS CGeol*
		M McCormac
		K A T McPherson
		D L Ross *FGS CGeol*
		Dr R A Smith *FGS*
HSO	6(S)	P M Halpin
		A A M Irving
		Dr S C Loughlin
		Dr E A Pickett
ASO	8(S)	W S McLean
AO	8(A)	Mrs E M B Clark

Overseas

SSO	5(S)	Dr R A Hughes

Geological Survey of Northern Ireland

Belfast

Group Manager (Grd 6)

	3(S)	Dr R A B Bazley *FGS CGeol*
PSec	8(A)	Mrs J Johnston
Grd 7	4(S)	Dr I C Legg
		Dr W I Mitchell
SSO	5(S)	T P Johnston
		D M Reay
HSO	6(S)	Dr M R Cooper *FGS*
SO	7(S)	W A Smyth
		G O Warke

Central England and Wales

Keyworth

Group Manager (Grd 6)

	3(S)	T J Charsley
PSec	8(A)	Mrs C A Searle
Grd 7	4(S)	Dr R Addison *FGS CGeol*
		W J Barclay *FGS CGeol*
		Dr A Brandon
		D McC Bridge
		Dr J N Carney *FGS CGeol*
		Dr A H Cooper *FGS CGeol*
		Dr B W Glover
		Dr A S Howard
		R D Lake
		Dr J H Powell *FGS CGeol*
		Dr R A Waters
		Dr D Wilson
SSO	5(S)	K Ambrose
		R G Crofts
		Dr C N Waters *FGS CGeol*
		Dr S R Young
HSO	6(S)	J M Hudson
		R S Lawley
		Dr J K Prigmore
		Dr P R Wilby
SO	7(S)	Mr E Hough
ASO	8(S)	Mrs M C Aldiss✳
		Mrs A J Lumb
		B Napier

† *Staff are grouped according to 1996 organisation.*

Overseas

SSO 5(S) Dr W T Pratt

Based at University of Wales, Aberystwyth

Grd 7 4(S) Dr J R Davies *FGS CGeol*

Southern and Eastern England

Keyworth

Group Manager (Grd 6)
    3(S) Dr I R Basham *FIMM CEng*
PSec 8(A) Mrs E A Cross
Grd 7 4(S) S J Booth
    J I Chisholm *FGS CGeol*
    R A Ellison *FGS CGeol*
    Dr R J O Hamblin *FGS CGeol*
    Dr B S P Moorlock
    P J Strange *FGS CGeol MIMM CEng*
    M G Sumbler *FGS CGeol*
SSO 5(S) A J M Barron *FGS CGeol*
    P M Hopson *FGS CGeol*
    Dr A A Jackson
    D H Jeffery *Eur Geol FGS CGeol*
    S J Mathers
    A N Morigi
    A Smith
    Dr R K Westhead *FGS CGeol*
    Dr I T Williamson
HSO 6(S) Dr A R Farrant
    A J Humpage
    Dr A Pedley
SO 7(S) R T Mogdridge

Overseas

Grd 7 4(S) Dr D T Aldiss *FGS CGeol*

Exeter

Grd 7 in charge
    4(S) Dr C R Bristow
PSec 8(A) Miss K A Patrick
Grd 7 4(S) Dr C M Barton
    Dr R A Edwards
    Dr R W Gallois *FGS CGeol FIMM CEng*
    Dr M T Holder *FGS CGeol*
    Dr B E Leveridge *FGS CGeol*
SSO 5(S) A J J Goode
HSO 6(S) Dr A J Newell
ASO 8(S) Mrs C P Smith

Regional Geophysics

Keyworth

Group Manager (Grd 6)
    3(S) Dr M K Lee *FGS CGeol*
PSec 8(A) Mrs S M Carter¶
    Mrs M Richards¶
Grd 7 4(S) Dr N R Brereton *FGS CGeol MIP CPhys*
    R M Carruthers
    Dr J D Cornwell
    Z K Dabek
    Dr C J Evans
    G S Kimbell
    K E Rollin
    I F Smith

SSO 5(S) B C Chacksfield
    R Pedley
    J P Williamson
HSO 6(S) Mrs S F Kimbell¶
    C P Royles
    A S D Walker
SO 7(S) Miss R E Heaven
    A Kingdon
ASO 8(S) D J R Morgan

Murchison House

Grd 7 in charge
    4(S) Dr J R Evans
SSO 5(S) J W F Edwards
    A S Mould
SO 7(S) A J Gibberd
ASO 8(S) Mrs P White

Overseas

Grd 7 4(S) M J Sankey☆

Data and Digital Systems

Keyworth

Group Manager (Grd 7)
    4(S) I Jackson
Grd 7 4(S) J R A Giles *FGS CGeol*
SSO 5(S) Dr D J Lowe *FGS CGeol*
HSO 6(S) J R Gibson
    Ms J C Walsby
SO 7(S) G R Baker
    Miss H J Baxendale
    E J Lewis
    A P Marchant
ASO 8(S) V J Hulland
    P J Molineaux
    Miss A R Storr
AO 8(A) Mrs S J A Chew

Murchison House

SSO 5(S) E P Smith
    K A Holmes
HSO 6(S) K I G Lawrie
SO 7(S) Mrs C M L Reynolds
ASO 8(S) Mrs K M Kilpatrick

Honorary Research Associate

    Dr M F Howells

PETROLEUM GEOLOGY, GEOPHYSICS AND OFFSHORE SURVEYS

Offshore geological and geophysical mapping, geophysical monitoring, and petroleum geology. Research and development in geomagnetism, marine and coastal geology, biostratigraphy and sedimentology, petroleum, global seismology, marine operations and databases. The maintenance of appropriate specialised facilities and databases.

Murchison House

Assistant Director (Grd 5)
    2(S) Dr C W A Browitt
PSec 8(A) Miss L M Nisbet

Petroleum Geology and Basin Analysis

Keyworth

Group Manager (Grd 6)
    3(S) Dr A Whittaker *FGS CGeol*

PSec 8(A) *vacancy*
Grd 7 4(S) R A Chadwick
    Dr S Holloway *FGS CGeol*
    Dr G A Kirby
    Dr T C Pharaoh *FGS CGeol*
    N J P Smith *FGS CGeol*
SSO 5(S) J Bulat
    Dr D J Evans
    W J Rowley
HSO 6(S) Dr H E Baily
SO 7(S) A G Hulbert
ASO 8(S) Miss K L Shaw

Murchison House

Grd 7 in charge
    4(S) Dr N G T Fannin
PSec 8(A) Ms R A R Aitken¶
Grd 7 4(S) R W Gatliff *FGS CGeol*
    H Johnson *FGS CGeol*
    J L McInnes
    Dr P C Richards *FGS CGeol*
    J D Ritchie
HSO 6(S) Mrs S M Jones
    M F Quinn
EO 7(A) A F Henderson

Gilmerton

Programme Manager (Grd 7)
    4(S) Mrs S J Stoker
Grd 7 4(S) Dr T D J Cameron
    K Smith
SSO 5(S) I J Andrews
    M C Smith
AO 8(A) M B Kassyk

Marine Geology and Operations

Murchison House

Group Manager (Grd 6)
    3(S) D A Ardus *FGS CGeol*
PSec 8(A) Miss J C Fraser
Grd 7 4(S) Dr J A Chesher
    Dr D Evans *FGS CGeol*
    K Hitchen *FGS CGeol*
    R Holmes
    D Long *FGS CGeol*
    J B Pheasant *MIEE CEng MIProdE CEng*
    A C Skinner *FGS CGeol*
    Dr M S Stoker *FGS CGeol*
SSO 5(S) C P Brett
    C C Graham
    A G Stevenson
HSO 6(S) Miss S A Alexander
    Dr P D Egerton
    N A Ruckley
    D J Smith *IEEIE*
    D G Wallis *MIEE CEng*
SO 7(S) Miss E J Gillespie
    J McGuigan
    G J Tulloch
HEO(c) 6(C) Mrs M W Sutherland *ALA*
    J B L Wild
EO(c) 7(C) Miss A E Richardson
AO 8(A) Mrs J A Meadows¶
PTO 7(T) N C Campbell
    J F Derrick
Tec 1 8(T) *vacancy*

Keyworth

Grd 7 4(S) D R Tappin

Coastal Geology

Keyworth

Group Manager (Grd 6)
    3(S) R S Arthurton
PSec 8(A) *vacancy*
Grd 7 4(S) Dr P S Balson
    Dr C D R Evans
    J W C James
    Dr J Ridgway *FGS CGeol*
    Dr R T R Wingfield
SSO 5(S) A Crosby *FGS CGeol*
    Dr J G Rees *FGS CGeol*
HSO 6(S) Dr D S Brew *FGS*
ASO 8(S) Mrs H M Glaves
    Miss A C Disney
    Mrs R Newsham
    Miss K E Outhwaite
    Mrs M P Slater
    Miss J M Woodhead✳

Overseas

Grd 7 4(S) B Humphreys

Biostratigraphy and Sedimentology

Keyworth

Group Manager (Grd 6)
    3(S) Dr B Owens
PSec 8(A) Mrs J Lines
Grd 7 4(S) Dr B M Cox *FGS CGeol*
    Dr R W O'B Knox
    Dr G K Lott
    Dr S G Molyneux
    A C Morton
    Dr J B Riding *FGS CGeol*
    Dr N J Riley *FGS CGeol*
    Dr A W A Rushton
    Dr G Warrington *FGS CGeol*
    Dr I P Wilkinson *FGS CGeol*
SSO 5(S) Dr N S Jones
    S P Tunnicliff
HSO 6(S) Miss C R Hallsworth¶
    Ms J C Hardiman
    Dr M Williams
    M A Woods
ASO 8(S) Mrs K L Johnson
    Miss J E Kyffin-Hughes
    Mrs P Taylor

Global Seismology

Murchison House

Group Manager (Grd 7)
    4(S) Dr D C Booth☆
PSec 8(A) Ms R A R Aitken¶
    Mrs A I Muir¶
Grd 7 4(S) Dr C D MacBeth
    Dr R M W Musson
    T Turbitt
    Miss A B Walker
SSO 5(S) J Laughlin
    Dr X Y Li
    Dr E Liu
    J H Lovell
    P C Marrow
    Mrs J A Richards¶
    Mrs M E A Ritchie¶
    Dr P W Wild
HEO(c) 6(C) Mrs J Exton
HSO 6(S) C J Fyfe
    S A Horne
    F Ohlsen
    Dr T J A Pointer

SO 7(S) G D Ford
D D Galloway
P H O Henni
R J Owen
Mrs F Wright¶
EO(c) 7(C) R J Carsley
ASO 8(S) B A Simpson
HPTO 6(T) D L Petrie
PTO 7(T) P S Day
D A Stewart
W A Velzian
R M Young

Geomagnetism
Murchison House
Group Manager (Grd 7)
4(S) Dr D J Kerridge
PSec 8(A) Mrs M Milne
Grd 7 4(S) D R Barraclough *MIP CPhys*
Dr T D G Clark
J C Riddick
SSO 5(S) Dr S MacMillan
HSO 6(S) S M Flower
T J Harris
E M Reader
Dr A W P Thomson *MIP CPhys*
SO 7(S) J G Carrigan
Miss E Clarke
C W Turbitt
ASO 8(S) J McDonald

Hartland
P&G 8(T) C R Pringle

Eskdalemuir
Tec 2 9(T) W E Scott
SBG2 9(T) Mrs M Scott¶

Honorary Research Associate
Dr J D Peacock
Mr D A Ardus

MINERALS AND GEOCHEMICAL SURVEYS
Mineral deposit studies, geochemical surveys, environmental geochemistry related to natural hazards, geochemical support for other divisions, specialist mineralogical, petrological and analytical geochemical laboratories, and comprehensive geochemical databases.

Keyworth
Assistant Director (Grd 5)
2(S) Prof J A Plant *FGS CGeol FIMM CEng*
PSec 8(A) Mrs K E Fairhurst
Mrs E A Szczerbiak*

Minerals
Keyworth
Group Manager (Grd 6)
3(S) G P Riddler *Eur. Ing. FIMM CEng MCIM MIMgt*
PSec 8(A) Mrs E Bishop¶
Mrs E J Simms¶
Grd 7 4(S) Dr G R Chapman *FGS CGeol*

Dr J S Coats *MIMM CEng*
T B Colman *MIMM CEng*
Dr D C Cooper *FGS CGeol*
A G Gunn
D E Highley *FGS CGeol MIMM CEng*
Dr R C Leake
SSO 5(S) R T Smith
HSO 6(S) D G Cameron
Dr G E Norton
M H Shaw
Ms L E Taylor
SO 7(S) Miss G L Collins
Mr B J Davies
Miss S F Hobbs
ASO 8(S) Miss K A Linley
EO 7(A) Miss M E Fellows
Miss J A Hillier
AO 8(A) Miss A J Mills
Miss R White

Murchison House
Grd 7 4(S) Dr C G Smith *MIMM CEng*

Exeter
Grd 7 4(S) Dr R C Scrivener *FGS CGeol*

Geochemistry
Keyworth
Group Manager (Grd 6)
3(S) Dr J W Baldock *MIMM CEng*
PSec 8(A) Mrs J Harrison
Grd 7 4(S) Dr J D Appleton *MIMM*
M J Brown *MIMM CEng*
P M Green
Dr H W Haslam *MIMM*
Dr C C Johnson *FGS CGeol*
Dr D G Jones *FGS CGeol*
Dr T M Williams
SSO 5(S) Dr N Breward
R C Jones *FGS CGeol*
P D Roberts
HSO 6(S) Ms D M A Flight
Ms F M Fordyce
Dr M G Hutchins
A C Mackenzie
C I Markle
B G Rawlins
G N Wiggans
SO 7(S) T R Lister
M H Strutt
D K Talbot *MRSC CChem*
ASO 8(S) K Barker
C Brettle
M W Cutler
A Ferguson
P&G 6(T) M A Allen
AO 8(A) Mrs T Shenton

Mineralogy and Petrology
Keyworth
Group Manager (Grd 6)
3(S) Dr D J Morgan *FGS CGeol*
PSec 8(A) Mrs P E Royall
Grd 6 3(I) Dr T J Shepherd (Individual merit)

Grd 7 4(S) Dr N J Fortey
D J Harrison *MIMM*
R J Merriman *FGS CGeol*
A E Milodowski *FGS CGeol*
G E Strong
Dr M T Styles *FGS CGeol*
SSO 5(S) D J Bland
Dr M R Gillespie
Dr P J Henney
K S Siddiqui
HSO 6(S) S D J Inglethorpe
S J Kemp
C J Mitchell
Dr J Naden
J M Pearce
SO 7(S) Dr V L Hards
P D Wetton
ASO 8(S) J M Careless*
R Carter
Miss E J Evans
J Fletcher
H A Murphy
PGS 6(T) D Oates

Murchison House
Grd 7 4(S) Dr B Beddoe-Stephens
SSO 5(S) Dr E K Hyslop
Dr E R Phillips
ASO 8(S) R D Fakes

Overseas
Grd 7 4(S) A J Bloodworth *FGS CGeol*★
D P Piper *FGS CGeol*★

Analytical Geochemistry
Keyworth
Group Manager (Grd 6)
3(S) D L Miles *MRSC Chem*
PSec 8(A) Miss C McDonald
Grd 7 4(S) Dr M R Cave *MRSC CChem*
Ms J M Cook *MRSC CChem*
R A Nicholson *MRSC CChem*
Dr B Smith *MRSCC CChem*
SSO 5(S) Miss L Ault
Dr S R N Chenery *MRSC CChem*
A E Davis
M N Ingham
HSO 6(S) Dr C J B Gowing
S Reeder
Mrs B P Vickers ¶
SO 7(S) P A Blackwell
A D Bradley
Mrs K A Green ¶
J J Robinson
J K Trick
ASO 8(S) Miss S E Brown
S J Carter
Miss R Naylor
Mrs K M Stevenson
Miss J Wragg

Honorary Research Associates
Mr P R Simpson
Mr P M Harris

GROUNDWATER AND GEOTECHNICAL SURVEYS
Hydrogeological, hydrogeochemical, geotechnical and related geophysical surveys and databasing. Research relating to exploration, development, management and protection of groundwater resources, to land disposal of hazardous wastes, and to civil engineering planning; and associated specialist laboratories.

Keyworth
Assistant Director (Grd 5)
2(S) Dr S S D Foster *FGS CGeol FIWEM MICE CEng*
PSec 8(A) Miss T K Blackwell

Hydrogeology
Wallingford
Group Manager (Grd 6)
3(S) I N Gale *FGS CGeol*★
PSec 8(A) Mrs C E Sharratt
Grd 6 3(I) Dr W M Edmunds (Individual merit)
Grd 7 4(S) B Adams *FGS CGeol*
D J Allen
D K Buckley
P J Chilton *FGS CGeol*
W G Darling
Dr D G Kinniburgh *MRSC CChem*
A R Lawrence *FGS CGeol*
B L Morris *FGS CGeol*
M Price *FGS CGeol MCIWEM*
N S Robins *FGS CGeol*
SSO 5(S) C S Cheney *FGS CGeol*
J Davies *FGS CGeol*
Miss R L Hargreaves
Mrs M A Lewis¶
A A Mckenzie
Dr P Shand
T R Shearer
Dr P L Smedley
Mrs M E Stuart
Mrs A T Williams
HSO 6(S) Dr J Bennett
M J Bird
Dr J P Bloomfield
A S Butcher
R Calow
Miss P Doorgakant¶
D C Gooddy
Dr H K Jones
D M J Macdonald
R J Marks
C J Milne *MRSC CChem*
Miss J M Trafford
SO 7(S) Mrs L J Brewerton
Miss L M Coleby
Ms S M Fenwick
Miss B R Gibbs
J C Talbot
Miss S J Wagstaff
ASO 8(S) J M Carrington
Miss K L Smith
P J Williams
AO 8(A) Mrs M Cole
vacancy

AA   9(A) Mrs A R Bailey
             M A Newman
SGB2 9(T) J M Sutton

Murchison House

SSO   5(S) D F Ball
HSO   6(S) A M Macdonald

Fluid Processes

Keyworth

Group Manager (Grd 6)
        3(S) Dr D M McCann *FGS*
             CGeol
PSec   8(A) Mrs D A Evans¶∗
             Mrs J M Mackrill
Grd 7 4(S) M P Hawkins
             Dr J J Higgo
             D C Holmes
             Dr P J Hooker *FGS*
             CGeol
             Dr S T Horseman
             Dr B A Klinck *MIMM*
             CEng
             Dr D J Noy
             Dr R P Shaw *FGS*
             CGeol MIMM CEng
             Dr J M West *MIB CBiol*
             G M Williams *FGS*
             CGeol
SSO   5(S) Dr M P Boland
             Dr R Metcalfe *FGS*
             CGeol
             Dr C A Rochelle
             Dr R S Ward
HSO   6(S) K Bateman
             S Dumpleton*FGS*
             CGeol
             J F Harrington
             I Harrison
             M A Sen∗
             G P Wealthall
SO   7(S) S J Baker
             Mrs P Coombs¶
             J R Davis
             Miss Y A Moore
             Miss L A Williams
ASO   8(S) Miss R U Leader
AO   8(A) Mrs C A Cole
AIO   7(T) Mrs L Gutteridge☆

Overseas

SSO   5(S) Dr S F Rogers

Engineering Geology and Geophysics

Keyworth

Group Manager (Grd 6)
        3(S) M G Culshaw *FGS*
             CGeol
PSec   8(A) Mrs J H Page¶
             vacancy
Grd 7 4(S) R Baria∗
             Dr D Beamish
             Dr J P Busby *FGS*
             CGeol
             A Forster *FGS*
             CGeol
             P G Greenwood *FGS*
             CGeol
             Dr P D Jackson *FGS*
             CGeol
             K J Northmore *FGS*
             CGeol
             Dr R D Ogilvy
             R J Peart
SSO   5(S) Dr T P Gostelow

             Dr D A Gunn
             J R Hallam
             P R N Hobbs
             S L Shedlock
HSO   6(S) A C Cripps
             Dr L J Donnelly
             D C Entwistle
             R C Flint
             P I Meldrum
             M G Raines
SO   7(S) L D Jones
             Mrs S J Self¶
PTO   7(T) G E Rippin
P&G   7(T) A M Barnes
AA   9(A) Mrs J L Meakin

NIREX Coordinator

Grd 6 3(S) Dr D W Holliday *FGS*
             CGeol ★

Honorary Research Associate

             Dr J A Barker
             Dr R A Downing

INTERNATIONAL AND MARKETING

Overseas work funded by the Overseas Development Administration, the EC, other multilateral funding agencies, and overseas governments. Coordination of BGS relationships with a wide range of international organisations, national geological surveys, and related agencies.

Keyworth

Assistant Director (Grd 5)
        2(S) Dr A J Reedman *FGS*
             CGeol
PSec   8(A) Mrs P S Musson
             Mrs L S Rathbone∗
HEO   6(A) Mrs C M Hurley
EO   7(A) Miss J Haslam
AO   8(A) Miss R M Hobson
             Miss C C Mills

Coordinator, BGS/ODA TDR Programme

Grd 7 4(S) Dr J D Bennett *FGS*
             CGeol MIMM

Africa, Middle East and South Pacific

Group Manager (Grd 6)
        3(S) A Macfarlane *FGS*
             CGeol
PSec   8(A) Mrs J Freeborough
Grd 7 4(S) P E J Pitfield *FGS*
             CGeol

Overseas

Grd 6 3(S) Dr P K Webb *FGS*
             CGeol
Grd 7 4(S) Dr R M Key *FGemm*
             MIMM
             Dr C Mortimer *Eur Ing*
             FIMM CEng

Asia and Latin America

Group Manager (Grd 6)
        3(S) R B Evans *FGS*
             CGeol

PSec   8(A) Mrs J Freeborough
Grd 7 4(S) P N Mosley

Overseas

Grd 6 3(S) Dr C J N Fletcher
             MIMM∗
Grd 7 4(S) Dr J A Aspden
             Dr S D G Campbell∗
             Dr P N Dunkley
             J A Fyfe∗
             Dr W J McCourt

Coordinator for Europe

Overseas

(Secretary General, EuroGeo Surveys)
Grd 7 4(S) Dr R N Annells *FIMM*
             CEng

Remote Sensing

Group Manager (Grd 7)
        4(S) Dr D Greenbaum
PSec   8(A) Ms A Coulson
Grd 7 4(S) Dr E A O'Connor
SSO   5(S) Dr S H Marsh
             Dr A J W McDonald
             A M Denniss
HSO   6(S) Dr D G Tragheim
SO   7(S) K B Greally

Hydrogeology Advisor to ODA

Wallingford

Grd 6 3(S) Dr R Herbert *FGS*
             CGeol
PSec   8(S) Miss S J Fairhurst

Mining Advisor to ODA

Grd 6 3(S) G P Walduck *FIMM*
             CEng

Marketing Coordination

Grd 6 3(S) Dr A J Wadge
PSec   8(A) Mrs P S Musson

Honorary Research Associate

             Dr E J Cobbing

CORPORATE COORDINATION AND INFORMATION

BGS information systems. Digital cartography, GISs and spatial modelling. Dissemination of information: library; map, book and report production and publication. Coordination of databases, management of corporate databases, and customer enquiries. R&D, training, and staff allocation.

Keyworth

Assistant Director (Grd 5)
        2(S) E F P Nickless *FGS*
             CGeol
PSec   8(A) Mrs J Swift *AIQPS*

Information Systems

Keyworth

Group Manager (Grd 6)
        3(S) D C Ovadia
PSec   8(A) Mrs G A Walters

SSO   5(S) K A McL Adlam
             B Cannell
HSO   6(S) Ms F Mclaren
             A T Riddick
SO   7(S) P D Bell
             A J Killen
             J S Sykes

Murchison House

Grd 7 4(S) J L Laxton
SSO   5(S) P G Robson
HSO   6(S) G Neilson
SO   7(S) T J E Holden
AO   8(A) M J Smith

Information Services

Keyworth

Group Manager (Grd 6)
        3(S) Dr A Dobinson
PSec   8(A) Mrs G A Walters

MARKETING AND PRODUCT DEVELOPMENT

BGS COPYRIGHT MANAGER

Keyworth

SSO   5(S) Dr J Alexander *MCIM*

COLLECTIONS ADMINISTRATION (MATERIALS)

Keyworth

Grd 7 4(S) S E Hollyer
SO   7(S) C W Wheatley
AO   8(A) Mrs J Wright ¶
Tec 1 8(T) D J Bennett
Tec 2 9(T) M D Naylor
             B Renshaw
             S Renshaw
             J R A Yates

COLLECTIONS ADMINISTRATION (DOCUMENTARY)

Library

Keyworth

PLib   4(L) G McKenna *ALA MIIS*
SLib   5(L) Mrs J E Anderson *ALA*¶
Lib   6(L) Miss J E Benson*ALA*
             Miss J V Bird *ALA*
             Mrs J Fileman *ALA*
             Miss J Hurst *ALA*
ALib   7(L) S J Prince *ALA*
AO   8(A) Mrs J A Barkworth
             Mrs N Gaffney
             Mrs L J Langton¶
             Ms Y J Oldham¶
             M C Swift
SGB2 9(T) Mrs S A Hodges
             G C Holley¶
Ty   9(A) Ms F Yarwood

Murchison House

Lib   6(L) R P McIntosh
             Mrs G E Gray
Records
Keyworth

HSO   6(S) R C Bowie
AO   8(A) Mrs S J Blatherwick
             Miss J H Booth
             Mrs G Bridge
             Mrs L J Fitch
             Mrs T L Heard
             W T Newham
             R L Widdison
AA   9(A) J J Davis

Murchison House

SO	7(S)	R J Gillanders
AO	8(A)	Miss A Dunlop
		A Morrison
		M S Swanney

BOREHOLE DATABASE

Keyworth

SO	7(S)	Mrs J H Bowie✳
		K C Stirland

CUSTOMER SERVICES

Keyworth

SSO	5(S)	Ms J J Parnham *ALA*
HSO	6(S)	A R Clayton
EO	7(A)	I K Page
AO	8(A)	Mrs J M Harvey
		Miss J L Hinde
		Mrs C Murray
		Mrs C G Robson
		Miss J J Self
		Mrs S D Roach
		Mrs H P Wiseman¶
SG	9(T)	S J Goodman
		vacancy
		Mrs P Wafforne¶

Murchison House

AO	8(A)	Mrs L Turnbull
Ty	9(A)	Mrs W J Moir

London office

HSO	6(S)	Miss S J Brackell
SO	7(S)	Mrs V R Messenger

ENQUIRIES OFFICER

Keyworth

SSO	5(S)	A D Evans

Publication Services Group

Keyworth

Group Manager (Grd 7)		
	4(S)	Dr C A Green
PSec	8(A)	Mrs M V Gardner¶

BOOK PRODUCTION

Keyworth

SSO	5(S)	Miss M B Simmons
AIO	7(T)	J P Stevenson
GO	7(T)	Mrs D C Rayner
SM3	8(T)	Ms J B A Evans
		A R Minks
		Ms J Norman

Ty	9(A)	Mrs A R Hutchinson
		Mrs A Morton
SM3	8(T)	J B Smedley

CARTOGRAPHIC PRODUCTION (S)

Keyworth

SMCO	5(M)	K H Becken
HMCO	6(M)	R J Parnaby
		S J Rippon
MCO	7(M)	Mrs C F Adkin
		J W Arbon
		Mrs K A Arbon ¶
		R W Armstrong
		M R Bowker
		Miss S Bray
		I L Cooke
		R J Cooper✳
		Mrs D L Daley¶
		R J Demaine
		J D Hodgson
		S E Hurst
		P Lappage
		M B Ledgard
		Mrs C H Mawer
		Mrs S B Myers ¶
		J I Rayner
		Mrs E J Scott
		Mrs C Simpson
		N A Spencer
		P Turner
		C Wardle
		I J Wilkinson
		Miss S E Wood
MCT 1	8(M)	Miss M A Bradley
		Mrs J E Kmieciak
		G J Tuggey
		S C Wilkinson

Overseas

HMCO	6(M)	C G Murray★

CARTOGRAPHIC PRODUCTION (N)

Murchison House

SMCO	5(M)	R B Ramsay
HMCO	6(M)	A M Stewart
MCO	7(M)	Miss C Anderson
		Miss J Barclay
		A Blenkinsop
		Mrs M M Cherrie
		K F Herbertson
		S W Horsburgh
		R M Long
		J L Meikle
		Mrs L M Oliver
		C Ritchie
		Mrs C J Sanders
		Mrs S A L Wild¶
		G R Wood

MCT 1	8(M)	Mrs C E Carson
		W H Denholm
		E P Drennan

CARTOGRAPHIC DEVELOPMENT

Keyworth

SMCO	5(M)	K H Becken
HMCO	6(M)	A W Clifton
		A H Myers

Murchison House

HMCO	6(M)	K C Mennim

PHOTOGRAPHY

Keyworth

PhO	7(P)	T P Cullen
AA	9(A)	M Goddard

Murchison House

HPhO	6(P)	T S Bain
PhO	7(P)	F I MacTaggart

PROMOTIONS AND PUBLIC RELATIONS

Keyworth

Grd 7	4(S)	Dr M Litherland *FGS*
		CGeol MIMM CEng
		Dr B J Taylor
SSO	5(S)	Dr J E Thomas¶
PSec	8(A)	Mrs M V Gardner¶
IO	6(T)	Mrs H J Heason

Training and R&D Coordination

Keyworth

Coordinator (Grd 7)		
	4(S)	Dr I E Penn *FGS CGeol*
Grd 7	4(S)	Dr M J Crow *MIMM*
		CEng FGS CGeol
AO	8(A)	Mrs P I Hale
Ty	9(A)	Miss E J Yarwood

¶	Part-time
★	Temporary promotion
✳	On unpaid leave

Grade abbreviations

AA	Administrative Assistant
AIO	Assistant Information Officer
ALib	Assistant Librarian
AO	Administrative Officer
ASO	Assistant Scientific Officer
Cl	Cleaner
EO	Executive Officer
GO	Graphics Officer
GTG	Graphics Technical Grade
HEO	Higher Executive Officer
Hman	Handyman
HMCO	Higher Mapping and Charting Officer
HPhO	Higher Photographic Officer
HPTO	Higher Professional and Technical Officer
HSO	Higher Scientific Officer
IO	Information Officer
Lib	Librarian
MCO	Mapping and Charting Officer
MCT	Mapping and Charting Technical Grade
Mess	Messenger
P&G	Process and General
PhO	Photographic Officer
Pk	Paperkeeper
PLib	Principal Librarian
PSec	Personal Secretary
PTO	Professional and Technical Officer
SEO	Senior Executive Officer
SG	Support Grade
SLib	Senior Librarian
SMCO	Senior Mapping and Charting Officer
SMess	Senior Messenger
SO	Scientific Officer
SPSec	Senior Personal Secretary
SPTO	Senior Professional and Technical Officer
SSO	Senior Scientific Officer
StO	Stores Officer
Tech	Technical Grade
Tel	Telephonist
Ty	Typist

Appendix 5   Academic collaboration

The BGS collaborates with research institutes within the NERC and the other research councils. It also collaborates with other academic institutions in a worldwide network of research projects, which include contracted imput to the core programme and research and teaching arrangements. The following are examples:

Aberdeen Univ.: *Sandstone provenance studies; CASE student*
Athens Univ. (Greece): *Mineral exploration; Historical earthquake studies*
Bangor Univ. (Univ. of Wales): *Monitoring contamination levels in mussel shells; External examination; MSc course*
Barcelona, Inst. (Spain): *Mineral exploration*
Berne Univ. (Switzerland): *Upper Carboniferous stratigraphy; Low temperature mineralogy*
Bergen Univ. (Norway): *Software equipment development*
Birkbeck College (Univ. of London): *Geological applications of single particle analysis by ICP/AES; metamorphic surveys; BGS/University collaborative projects*
Birmingham Univ.: *BGS/University collaborative projects; aquifer studies*
Bradford Univ.: *Building stone properties; Extracting environmental information from corals; Dept. of Civil & Environmental Engineering, Advisory panel; organic pollutants in groundwater*
Brighton Univ.: *Chalk stratigraphy and geotecnics*
Bristol Univ.: *PhD supervision; Characterzation of dissolved organic carbon*
California Univ. (Santa Cruz): *petrology*
Camborne School of Mines: *Mineral processing; HND course*
Cambridge Univ.: *Stratigraphy of Welsh Basin; Studies of volcanic dusts and acid gas contamination; BGS/University collaborative projects*
Campinas Univ. (Brazil): *Seismic inversion studies*
Cardiff Univ. (Univ. of Wales): *Landfill gas migration*
Catalunya Univ. *Transport of gasses through the geosphere; PhD supervision*
Cincinatti Museum (USA): *Cambrian correlation and biogeography*
Cincinatti Univ. (USA): *bentonite research;*
Clermont-Ferrand Univ. (France): *Montserrat Volcanic Observatory*
CNRS, Toulouse, (France): *Microscale fluid mineral interations*
Cranfield Univ.: *Groundwater vulnerability map of England and Wales*
CREGU, Nancy, France: *Fluid inclusion research*
Coimbra Univ. (Portugal): *Mineral exploration*
Cologne Univ. (Germany): *Seismic monitoring*
CSIRO Fisheries Division (Australia): *Chemistry of the earbones of fish*
Czech Geological Survey: *Variscan geology & tectonics, mineralisation*
De Montfort Univ. (Leicester): *Dinantian stratigraphy*
Derby Univ.: *Quaternary geology of Trent and Derwent valleys; LOIS collaboration; PhD*
Dublin Trinity College (Ireland): *Carboniferous palynology*
Durham Univ.: *Montserrat Volcanic Observatory; LOIS collaboration; BGS/University collaborative projects; Coral palaeocology, Conodont stratigraphy of Dent Group*
East Anglia Univ.: *LOIS collaboration; PhD supervision*
Edinburgh Napier Univ.: *Sandwich students*
Edinburgh Univ.: *Namurian stratigraphy and seimentology; Sandwich students; 3-D seismics; GIS systems; recurrence statistics PULSE programme*
Exeter Univ.: *External examiner*
Flinders Univ.: *(S Australia); PhD supervision*
Frankfurt Univ. (Germany): *Earthquake prediction*
Freiburg Univ.: *Upper Carboniferous stratigraphy*
Glasgow Univ.: *BGS/University collaborative projects; PhD supervision*
Greenwich Univ.: *Scottish Highlands mapping*
Groningen K.V. Inst. (The Netherlands): *Environmental radioactivity*
Hamburg Univ.: *Seismic software development*
Heriot Watt Univ.: *Seismic modelling, reservoir studies and anistropy at the reservoir scale*
Hull Univ.: *LOIS collaboration; Advisor on geochemistry course*
Imperial College (Univ. of London): *PhD supervision; CASE student*
Keele Univ.: *Montserrat Volcanic Observatory, Upper Carniferous stratigraphy; Triassic palynomorph taphonomy, Seismic monitoring*
Kingston Univ.: *Visiting professor, hydrogeology; Geochemistry of chalk sediments; lecture course*
Krackow Univ. (Poland): *Natural gas composition in NW Europe*
Lancaster Univ.: *Montserrat Volcanic Observatory; Chemical denitrification*

Leeds Univ.: *Montserrat Volcanic Observatory; Gold research; Geochemical modelling; TEM studies; LOIS collaboration*
Leicester Univ.: *Shallow seismic survey of Triassic unconformity (Charnwood); Wenlock graphtolite biozones of Builth mudstones; MSc projects; Sedimentology: industrial minerals; Mineral processing; Cambrian biostratigraphy; Ordovician acritarch stratigraphy*
Liege Univ. (Belgium): *Palaeozoic palynology, Carboniferous stratigraphy*
Leipzig Univ. (Germany): *Quaternary geology*
Liverpool Univ.: *Ashgill glaciouestatics; Visiting Professor, PhD supervision; BGS/University collaborative projects; LOIS collaboration*
Loughborough Univ.: *Humic substances and the migration of radionuclides*
Luton Univ.: *External examiner (HND courses)*
Manchester Univ.: *TEM studies*
Michigan Univ. (USA): *TEM studies*
Montpelier Univ. (France): *Lower Cretaceous stratigraphy*
Naples Univ. (Italy): *Clay analogues*
Napier Univ. (Edinburgh): *Sandwich students*
Nevada Univ. (USA): *Mineral exploration*
New Bedford College: *Pleistocene geology; Aquifer studies*
New York State Univ.: *ODP-related studies*
Newcastle Univ.: *PhD and MSc supervision*
Nottingham Univ.: *Environmental mineralogy; DANPL clay interactions*
Nottingham Trent Univ.: *MSc course; Risk assessment study of soil geochemistry data*
Open Univ.: *Montserrat Volcanic Observatory; Study supervision; BGS/University collaborative projects*
Oxford Univ.: *Kimmeridgian stratigraphy; Hydrogeochemistry*
Oxford Bookes Univ.: *Upper Carboniferous sedimentology; Geochemistry*
Penn State Univ.: *Montserrat Volcanic Observatory*
Perugia Univ. (Italy): *Lower Jurassic Tethyan dinoflagellates*
Plymouth Univ.: *Foraminifera as indicators of heavy metal pollution; Engineering geology maps*
Portsmouth Univ.: *BGS/University collaborative projects*
Queen's Univ. (Belfast): *PhD supervision*
Reading Univ.: *Montserrat Volcanic Observatory; LOIS collaboration; Kimmeridgian climates; Hydrogeology MSc course; CASE Studentship; Seismic properties of sea-floor rocks and sediments; Geochemical studies*
Rome Univ.: *Natural analogues of clay backfills in adioactive waste repositories; Gas migration through the geosphere; clay analogues*
Royal Holloway College, (Univ. of London): *Trace element geochemistry; Pleistocene geology–East Anglia; PhD and MSc supervision; Geomicrobiological lectures; Visiting Professor of Contaminant Hydrogeology; Hydrogeochemistry of selenium*
Scotland, National Museum: *Archaeological petrology*
Sheffield Univ.: *Palaeogene stratigraphy; Delivering the module ESC326; PhD supervision MSc course in aspects of waste disposal; BGS/University collaborative projects; Silurian–Permian palynology; Associate professor; Engineering geological mapping*
Siberian Academy of Science: *Granite petrology*
Southampton Univ.: *LOIS collaboration; Honorary positions; PhD supervision; Hydrogeochemistry*
St Andrews Univ.: *bentonite research*
Stirling Univ.: *Sandwich students; Potential for aquaculture using saline groundwater*
Strathclyde Univ.: *Scottish Highlands mapping*
Surrey Univ.: *MSc course*
Sydney Univ.: *Great Barrier Reef drilling*
Toulouse Univ. (France): *Microscale fluid mineral interactions*
Thessaloniki Univ. (Greece): *Seismic monitoring Seismic monitoring; seismic hazard studies*
University College (Univ. of London): *Chalk groundwater study; external examiner; Upper Jurassic stratigraphy; PhD examiner; CASE studentship supervision; Metamorphic surveys; MSc course; Nitrate pollution*
Uppsala Univ. (Sweden): EUROPROBE *directorate*
Vinogradov Institute of Geochemistry: *Granite geochemistry*
Vrije Univ. (Amsterdam): *PhD supervision*
Wageningen Univ. (the Netherlands): *PhD supervision*
Zaragoza University: *Gypsum dissolution geohazards*

Appendix 6   Business collaboration

COLLABORATION WITH UK AND INTERNATIONAL INDUSTRIES

The BGS maintains a wide range of links with industry. These involve co-funded projects, technology partnerships, strategic business alliances and advisory groups. The following include most of the companies who collaborated:

- AEA Technology, Harwell
- Amerada Hess
- Amoco
- A–Z
- BEB Erdgas und Erdol GmbH
- BHP Minerals
- British Antarctic Survey
- Brittania Aggregates Ltd
- British Gas
- British Gypsum
- Carmarthen District Council
- Ceredigion District Council
- City & County of Swansea, Dept of Highways Technical and Property Services
- Christison Scientific (development of new milling media)
- Conoco
- Conterra AB, Sweden
- Department of Geophysics, Uppsala University, Sweden (EUROPROBE directorate)
- DRA
- Dyfed County Council
- East Lothian District Council
- Elf
- Ensign Geophysics
- Entec UK Ltd
- Environmental Agency
- European Science Foundation, Strasbourg (EUROPROBE funding agency)
- Exmoor National Park
- Exxon
- Instituto Geológico e Mineiro, Portugal
- Instituto Tecnológico GeoMinero, Spain
- Geological Survey of Greece
- GeoRisk
- GeoScience Ltd
- Geotechnical Engineering Office Hong Kong
- Golder Associates
- Knight & Piesold
- Mobil
- NAM
- Nirex
- Nottingham University
- Ove Arup
- Preseli Pembroke District Council
- Price & Myers Ltd
- QuantiSci
- RJB Mining plc
- R Maddoch, Consultant
- Roger Tym & Partners
- Ruddington Grange Golf Club
- Saga Petroleum
- Schlumberger
- Serep

- Shell
- Silver & Barytes
- Soil Survey
- Tarmac-Soletanche Ltd
- Titan Cement
- Total

CLIENT LIST

UK Government

- Bath City Council
- Calderdale District Council
- City and County of Swansea, Dept. Of highways, Technical and Property Services
- Coal Authority
- Cornwall County Council
- Countryside Commission
- Cumbria County Council
- Darlington District Council
- Defence Research Agency (DRA)
- Department of Economic Development (Northern Ireland)
- Department of the Environment (DOE)
- Department of Trade and Industry
- Department of Transport
- DoE–Minerals and Waste Planning Division
- DTI–Engineering, Automotive and Metals Division
- Durham County Council
- DWI
- EA
- East Lothian District Council
- EC
- English Heritage
- English Nature
- EPSRC
- Foreign and Commonwealth Office
- Harrogate Borough Council
- Health and Safety Executive
- Joint Nature Conservancy Council
- Kent County Council
- Laboratory of Government Chemist
- London Borough of Newham
- MAFF
- Magnox Electric plc
- Metropolitan Police
- Ministry of Agriculture, Fisheries and Food
- Ministry of Defence
- National Rivers Authority
- National Trust
- Natural History Museum
- NERC
- Newham Borough Council
- Northumberland County Council
- Nuclear Installations Inspectorate
- NRA
- Overseas Development Administration
- Office for National Statistics
- Office of Science and Technology
- Scottish Natural Heritage
- Scottish Office
- Sheffield University

- SNIFFER
- SOAEFD
- States of Jersey
- Renfrewshire District Council
- UK Government
- UK Nirex
- Welsh Office
- West Devon Borough Council
- West Sussex County Council

International

- AGSO
- Andra, France
- Commission of the European Community
- Commission for Lands and Environment, Zanzibar
- Department of Mining and Petroleum, Papua New Guinea
- European Union INTAS Projects
- Falklands Island Government
- Geological Survey of Ireland
- Geotechnical Engineering Office, Hong Kong
- Government of Hong Kong,
- Government of Papua New Guinea
- Hong Kong Geological Survey
- Hong Kong Government
- IAEA
- INTAS
- NAGRA (Switzerland)
- OECD/NEA
- PNC (Japan)
- Roma University
- Royal Netherlands Government
- UNESCAP (United Nations Economic and Social Commmission for Asia and the Pacific)
- USGS
- WHO/UNEP
- World Bank (WB)
- World Bank

Industry

- Advance Geophysical
- AEA Technology
- AECL, Canada
- Agip
- A H Leech Son & Dean
- Airport Authority, Hong Kong
- All Company in the BGS Rockall Consortium
- Amalgamated Mining Industries
- Amerada Hess Ltd
- Amerada Hess Ltd
- Amoco (UK) Exploration Company
- Amoco (UK) Exploration Ltd
- Amoco
- Anadrill Schlumberger
- Anamet
- ANDRA
- Anglian Water
- Anglo Pacific Resources
- Anardarko Petroleum Corporation

- Applied Geotechnical Engineering Ltd
- ARC, Bardon Roadstone
- ARC Northern
- ARCO British Ltd
- ARCO International Oil & Gas
- ARK Geophysics
- Asturiana de Zinc, SA, Spain
- Babcock Water Engineering
- Baker Hughes INTEQ
- BEB Erdgas und Erdol Gmbh
- BFI Ltd
- BHP Minerals Ltd.
- BHP Petroleum Ltd
- Blue Circle Cement
- Borax Consolidated
- BP Exploration Operating Co. Ltd
- BP Norge Ltd.
- BPB Gypsum Limited
- Bristol University
- British Gypsum
- British Gas Exploration and Production Ltd
- British Nuclear Fuels plc
- Bryant Homes
- Brodie Forbes Partnership
- BT Marine plc
- Bureau de Recherches Géologique et Minière
- Buxton Lime Industries Ltd
- Cambourne School of Mines
- Cambridge University
- Candecca Resources Ltd
- Castle Cement Ltd
- CEA (France)
- Celtic Technologies
- Challenge Environmental Partnership
- Charmer Technical University
- Clayton Environmental Consultants Ltd
- Chevron UK Ltd
- CIRIA
- Clyde Petroleum plc
- Cold Gold Ltd
- Completely Stoned Ltd
- Conoco UK Ltd
- Cooper Associates
- Crediton Minerals Ltd
- Crouch, Hogg, Waterman
- CSIRO (Australia)
- Cundall, Johnston and Partners
- Danish Geodetic Institute
- Deakin, Callard and Partners
- Deepwood Mining Co. Ltd
- DEMAS Dredging Consultants
- Deminex UK Oil and Gas Ltd
- Doyle Partnership
- EA Technology
- Econ Consult
- Elf Enterprise Caledonia Ltd
- Elf Exploration UK
- EMU Pumps (UK) Ltd
- Enterprise Oil
- Enterprise Oil plc
- Environment Agency
- Essex and Suffolk Water
- Esso Exploration and Production Ltd
- Esso Exploration & Production UK Ltd
- Exxon Exploration Incorporated

- Fina
- Fluor Daniel Limited
- Fordamin Co. Ltd
- Fosroc
- Gandil Agricultural Co. Ltd
- GECO-PRAKLA
- GEM Services
- Geochem Group Ltd
- Geonex Aeroservice
- Geoteam AS
- Geotechnical Developments
- Geotek Ltd
- Greenwich Resources Ltd
- GU Projects
- Halliburton Energy Services
- H J Banks
- HR Wallingford Ltd
- Hunting Aquatic Resources
- Hyder Environmental
- Hydrographic Office
- Hydraulics Research
- Hyundai Engineering & Construction
- ICI
- Jersey New Waterworks
- John Brown Engineering & Construction Ltd
- Joint Nature Conservation Committee
- Kalahari Gold and Copper Ltd
- Kerr-McGee Oil (UK) Ltd
- Laing Technology Group Ltd
- Lasmo North Sea plc
- Leeds University
- Location Sample Services Inc
- LTG
- Maersk Directional Drilling
- MAFF
- Marathon Internation Petroleum (GB) Ltd
- Maunsell & Partners
- Metropolitan Police
- McDonald Institute
- Mid Kent Water
- MI Drilling Fluids
- Mobil
- Mobil North Sea Ltd
- Monument Oil and Gas plc
- Murphy Petroleum Ltd
- Nagra, Switzerland
- NAM
- Norwegian Crystallites AS
- Nuclear Electric plc
- Nuclear Installations Inspectorate (NII)
- Odin Mining International
- Omya, Croxton + Garry Ltd
- Ove Arup
- Pancanadian Petroleum
- Pennant Plant
- Perry Equipment Ltd
- Peters Associates
- PGS Exploration AS
- Phillips Petroleum
- Phillips Petroleum Co. UK Ltd
- PNC, Japan
- Polish Geological Institute
- Posford Duvivier
- PowerGen
- Price & Myers Ltd

- Quaternary TL Surveys,
- Ranger Oil (UK) Ltd
- Readymix Concrete
- Redland Aggregates Ltd
- RJB Mining
- Rockall Consortium
- Roxburgh and Partners
- RTZ Ltd
- Ruddington Grange Golf Club
- Rugby Cement Ltd
- Rutter Johnson Partnership
- Saga Petroleum ASA
- Saudi Arabian Oil Company
- SAUR
- Schlumberger Geco-Prakla
- Scottish Hydro-Electric plc
- Scottish Nuclear Ltd
- Scott Wilson Kirkpatrick,
- Scott Wilson Kirkpatrick Ltd
- SCK. CEN. (Belgium)
- Sedgwick Europe Ltd
- SEPA
- Setco Services Pte., Singapore
- Severn Trent Water
- Shell
- Shell UK Exploration and Production Ltd
- Simag AS (Norway)
- Sir William Halcrow and Partners
- SKB, Sweden
- Soil Mechanics Ltd
- Southern Scottish Goldfields Ltd
- Spectrum Energy and Information Technology Ltd
- Sperry-Sun Drilling Services
- SPS Technologies
- Statens Kartverk
- Statoil (UK) Ltd
- Stratasearch Geological Consulting Ltd
- Symonds Travers Morgan
- Tarmac-Soletamche Ltd
- Tarmac Quarry Products Ltd
- Tarmac Roadstone
- Tertiary Gold Ltd
- Tertiary Gold and Copper
- Texaco Ltd
- Thames Water
- The National Grid Company plc
- Thornton Colquhoun
- T&N Technologies
- Total
- Total Oil Marine plc
- Turkish Petroleum
- Turkish Petroleum Corporation
- UKWIR
- UK Nirex Ltd
- Union Rail
- Unocal Ltd
- Valley Marine Researches
- Wascana
- Wessex Water
- Western Frontiers Association
- Western Geophysical
- Yorkshire Water

Appendix 7   The BGS Programme Board

REMIT

The BGS Programme Board was established in 1988 to determine the overall objectives and to set the priorities for the BGS Core Programme. It has acted as a 'surrogate customer' for the Office of Science and Technology, providing accountability for the way the BGS spends its Science Budget funding. The Programme Board approves the proposed work programme and deliverables each financial year. It also monitors progress toward achieving these deliverables. The Programme Board met four times during 1996/97.

TERMS OF REFERENCE

Having regard to the resources likely to be available, including those forthcoming from charging for goods and services, and to actual and likely commissions, the Board will advise the NERC on:

- the aims and objectives of a national geosciences survey;

- the long-term objectives of the BGS Core Programme, specifying timescales, required outputs and, in particular, priorities for a three year rolling programme beginning in 1990/91;

- having regard to these priorities, the definitive core programme for the financial year immediately ahead;

- the research programme recommended to be undertaken by the BGS to sustain and enhance its capability to achieve its objectives; and

- the case for changes in the resources required to undertake further work.

The Board monitors and reports to the NERC on the balance of core, contract and research work undertaken by the BGS and on the performance against the defined objectives and programme.

MEMBERSHIP

Board members are appointed by the Chief Executive of the NERC and serve three year terms of office. They are drawn from the BGS user community and include senior representatives of industry, government agencies and academia as listed below. The Director of the BGS, **Dr P J Cook**, and the Director of NERC Science and Technology, **Dr D J Drewry**, are also members, and the four government departments most concerned with the BGS provide Assessors. These are: the Office of Science and Technology; the Department of Trade and Industry; the Department of the Environment, Transport and the Regions; and the Department of Economic Development for Northern Ireland. The Secretariat is provided by **Mr D Hackett** and **Dr S H Marsh** of the British Geological Survey at Keyworth.

BOARD MEMBERS

Dr E R Hassall is the Chairman of the Programme Board and is also Deputy Chairman of the Coal Authority. He was formerly the Chairman of Wardell Armstrong and a Crown Mineral Agent. He previously worked in the Production and Mining Departments of the National Coal Board.

Prof D J Blundell is Professor of Environmental Geology at Royal Holloway, University of London. He has mainly researched in seismology and marine geopyhsics. He was a co-founder of the British Institutions Reflection Profiling Syndicate and took a leading role in the European Geotraverse supported by the European Science Foundation. He is a past President of the Geological Society.

Dr J V Bramley serves on the Councils of the Institution of Mining and Metallurgy, the Mining Association of the United Kingdom and the Mineral Industries Research Organisation. He was formerly the General Manager of Laporte Minerals and is a past President of the Institution of Mining and Metallurgy.

Dr J P B Lovell OBE is a Senior Research Fellow in Earth Sciences at Cambridge University. He was formerly Head of Recruitment at BP Exploration and is now a consultant to them. He previously held several senior positions within BP Exploration and, before this, was a lecturer at Edinburgh University.

Dr C J Morrissey is Group Chief Geologist, Western Hemisphere, for Rio Tinto. He was formerly Managing Director of RTZ Mining and Exploration in Europe and held several other senior positions. Before this he was a Research Fellow at Imperial College London and Lecturer in Economic Geology at the Royal School of Mines.

Mr J Mortimer is Technical and External Affairs Director at ARC, for whom he has held a number of other positions in production management. He is Chairman of the CBI Minerals Committee, the BACMI Public Affairs Committee, and is on the organising committee for Minerals Week in 1998.

Mr D R Norbury is Head of Engineering Geology at Soil Mechanics. He is currently Chairman of the Working Party on Rock Weathering convened by the Engineering Group of the Geological Society. He has sat on the Geological Society's Council and has been Treasurer of their Engineering Group.

Dr A C Skinner is Pollution Prevention and Control Manager for the Midlands Region at the Environment Agency. He is the Secretary General of the International Association of Hydrogeologists and was formerly the Head of the National Groundwater Centre for the National Rivers Authority.

Prof G Walton is the Senior Partner at the Geoffrey Walton Practice and a Visiting Professor at Leeds University. He was formerly the Headquarters Geotechnical Engineer for the National Coal Board's Opencast Executive, and was also seconded to the Rock Mechanics Research Group at the Royal School of Mines.

Appendix 8   Core Programme Achievements

At its meeting on 13 June 1997, the BGS Programme Board was presented with a review of the 1996/97 core programme; a summary of its achievements follows:

ONSHORE AND GEOPHYSICAL SURVEYS

A1 — Multidisciplinary Regional Surveys

General

- 3559 square kilometres resurveyed and revised.
- 217 1:10 000 standards (manually drawn) approved for public use.
- 30 1:10 000 standards (digital) approved.
- 102 technical reports for calendar year 1996.
- The 1:50 000 Keswick sheet (29) completed ahead of schedule.
- 26 1:50 000 sheets approved for submission to Publication Services.
- 5 memoirs approved for submission to Publication Services.

Co-funded Projects

- Afon Teifi project remains on schedule; 8 1:25 000 part standards completed and drawn. Partners: 5 Welsh District Councils.
- Desk revision of drift linework in an area west of Inverness to compile digital data on sand and gravel resources completed. Partner: Inverness District Council.
- Memoir for the geology of West Cumbria, on schedule to complete in 1997/98. Partner: Nirex.
- Desk revision of Coal Measures in Midland Valley to compile digital linework for resources GIS, in progress. Partners: Scottish Natural Heritage, East Lothian District Council.

A2 — Continuous Revision

Data Acquisition and Map Revision, Highland and Islands

- Revision of drift maps around Aberdeen and Inverness.

Data Acquisition and Map Revision, Scottish Lowlands and Northern England

- 22 digital 1:10 000 maps of Glasgow corrected and issued.
- 132 boreholes in Midland Valley were logged and sampled, total 3685 metres.
- 3 Midland Valley opencast sites monitored; 6 temporary sections logged.

Data Acquisition and Map Revision, Central England and Wales

- Continuous revision in South and West Yorkshire now organized; 4 1:10 000 standards around Barnsley revised.
- 15 digital 1:10 000 maps of Wrexham corrected and issued.

Data Acquisition and Map Revision, Southern and Eastern England

- 13 1:10 000 maps of Bristol revised; one transferred from County Series.
- 5 1:10 000 digital maps of London corrected and issued; 2 reissued as Version 2.

Digital Mapping Development

- Prototype automated enquiry answering system (ALGI) developed and handed over for production.
- Digital Map Compilation System (DMCS) prototype system developed and put to test.
- PC-based GIS for geologist desks — software evaluated.
- Digital map production system (DMPS) upgraded.
- Field notebook — Version 1 delivered.

A3 — Onshore Surveys Database

Database and Computing Support

- Help desk has been in full use supporting some 200 PCs, 25 Unix workstations and other equipment.
- Vax conversion progressed nearly on schedule; applications relating to borehole databases remain to be converted.
- Lexicon new entry and browsing facilities designed using ACCESS and EXCEL. Print-on- demand facility developed.
- Rock classification scheme database now contains the igneous rocks scheme.
- Database and front end for 1:10K map sales delivered.

A5 — Regional Geophysical Surveys

Regional Crustal Structure

- CD-ROM for Northern Britain is completed and ready for internal review.
- Interpretation of Southern Scotland and Northern England is well under way.

Geophysical Computing Support and Development

- Migration from VAX to Unix workstations is complete.
- Upgrades have been carried out on

COLMAP, WELLOG and ARARAT software.
- Major developments have been made in the suite of 3-D gravity/magnetic modelling programs.
- PC-GRAVMAG has been implemented to run under Windows.

Refraction Studies

- Modelling software converted to run on SG workstations.
- Wide-angle seismic surveys for imaging sub-basalt structure reviewed.

National Geophysical Mapping and Data Management

- Shetland gravity survey completed.
- Two 1:1 million gravity sheets (Shetland and North Sea) submitted for publication.
- Transfer of gravity data to Unix file server completed.

Co-funded Projects

- Magnetic properties of sedimentary rocks — project completed. Magnetic susceptibility data acquired from 70 boreholes.
- Geomechanical properties of rockmass — project completed.
- FieldBank — project ongoing.

HYDROCARBONS, OFFSHORE SURVEYS AND GEOPHYSICAL MONITORING

B1 — Offshore Surveys

Rockall Continental Margin

- The consortium has chosen to extend its remit for a further year, and contract extensions have been submitted for 1997/98. Twelve companies are now members and approaches have been made to a further three. Work completed during the year includes:
  — Geophysical Image Atlases Volumes 11G & 11M — Hatton Bank (Gravity) and Hatton Bank (Magnetic) have been prepared and presented to the Rockall Consortium.
  — A report has been completed on the petrography of Early Tertiary volcanic rocks in well 154/3–1.
  — Reports have been prepared on the reprocessing of BGS seismic data on Rockall Bank, a geological appraisal of the Hatton–Rockall Trough and Late Cretaceous to Early Tertiary igneous activity in the Northern Rockall Trough.

— Organization and planning is in hand for a major two ship seismic and OBS experiment to image beneath the basalts in the Rockall Trough.

Western Frontiers Association

- A consortium including 15 companies and HSE is in place to March 1998 (with a procedure to establish a rolling commitment) to further understanding of shallow geology and ground conditions on the shelf margin and slope.
- Projects undertaken include a comprehensive computerised bibliography; slope stability; clathrates, geohazards; shallow gas; extension of the national seismic grid to look westward.

Offshore Map Production

- 1:250 000 solid geology sheets for Wight, Moray Firth and Tyne Tees have been printed.
- Shetland Seabed Sediments is in final stages of preparation in the Drawing Office.
- Sula Sgeir Solid Geology is undergoing final editing before submission to Drawing Office.
- Work is in hand on the following 1:250 000 sheets:
  - Shetland Quaternary is in final stages of preparation.
  - The Guernsey Solid Geology and Quaternary are complete except for final input of data from the French.

Development Of The Offshore Database

- Work on the core archive facility continues including transfer of core from Keyworth to make space for the land core from the DTI store.
- Data continues to be reviewed from the Hydrographic Office.

Marine Operational Capability

- The MAST II Hammer Corer prototype trials were satisfactory completed and the corer has been prepared for full scale trials in the Indian Ocean by German partners.
- The corer for NERC/BRIDGE to take orientated samples for palaeomagnetic studies of mid- ocean ridges is nearly complete and trials are planned for June 1997.

Corsaires

- The Corsaires initiative, which aims to provide EC programmes with the facility to undertake offshore drilling, is funded for a further year.

B2 — Coastal Surveys

Land-Ocean Interaction Study (LOIS)

- Comprehensive support has continued to be provided to the LOIS Special Topic community in respect of core curation and associated scientific services.
- Framework activities have produced a digital stratigraphic database, an analysis of the anthropogenic contaminant history of the LOIS focal study area, and have assessed contributions made to marine budgets from coastal erosion through the application of remote sensing techniques.

Strategic Nearshore Zone Survey

- Inner Thames Estuary 1:50 000 Coastal Geology Series map approved in final proof.
- Two sectors of the co-funded Inshore Seabed Characterisation Project, Shoreham–Dungeness and Flamborough Head–Gibraltar Point, have been completed and approved. A third sector, the Wash–Winterton, has been completed and awaits approval.

B3 — Petroleum Geology and Basin Analysis

- Maintenance and development of a stratigraphic surfaces database continues.
- Preparation of regional small-scale maps of key stratigraphic surfaces continues using digital methods. A set of general procedures has been established for production of these maps using in-house and commercial software. Initial compilations of base Tertiary/Top Chalk of the central and northern North Sea have been made.
- Interpretation of data from the Cheshire–Staffs Basin continues, concentrating on the pre- Mesozoic succession.

High Resolution Correlation

- A draft report on Upper Silurian (Ludlow) correlations in digital format was completed during 1996/97. This is an interactive report which links text and graphics (maps and vertical sections), enabling the user to investigate the correlation of Ludlow strata in the UK and the methods used to achieve correlation. The report establishes links between different methods of correlation, leading to holostratigraphic understanding of the series.
- Reports on correlations and correlation methods are in progress for the Rhaetian (upper Triassic), Callovian (Upper Jurassic) and Thanetian (Tertiary), joining reports completed on the Llandovery (Lower Silurian), Oxfordian (Upper Jurassic) and Albian (Lower Cretaceous).

Carboniferous Heavy Minerals

- Additional data have been acquired for the Carboniferous of central and northern England. Coverage of the Namurian to Westphalian succession of the Bradford area is now complete, and a report has been prepared.
- A pilot study on heavy mineral assemblages in the Carboniferous of the Midland Valley of Scotland has been completed and the data presented in a report.
- The analytical phase has been completed in the programme of U/Pb 'SHRIMP' dating of detrital zircons as a means of constraining source terrains.

B4 — Geophysical Monitoring

Geomagnetism

- New magnetic observatory systems commissioned on 1st January 1997.
- Automatic updating of the GIFS and INTERMAGNET on-line databases 7 days a week.
- Monthly bulletins for each of the UK magnetic observatories published within 7 days of month end.
- 1995 UK Magnetic Observatories' Yearbook published in May 1996.
- One-minute datasets for 1995 for the UK observatories and for the BGS stations on Ascension Island and the Falkland Islands archived on CD-ROM.
- Data processing for 1995 for Ascension Island and the Falkland Islands completed by June 1996 and Yearbooks published.
- 1996 Revision of the BGS Global Geomagnetic Model issued in April 1996.
- Eleven repeat stations occupied in the UK Magnetic Survey network.
- New UK regional main-field model produced.

Global Seismology

- Seventh Annual Monitoring Report (1995/96) published in June 1996.
- Monthly seismic event bulletins published 6 weeks in arrears for all months.
- UK earthquake bulletin for 1996 published in March 1997.
- Immediate felt event reports disseminated by fax.
- 204 Earthquakes located during the year 1996 (34 felt).
- Four significant earthquake reports in press.
- Macroseismic surveys undertaken after Penzance earthquake and Musselburgh tremors.
- All 141 seismic stations are on rapid access on-line systems.
- All stations have been resurveyed using GPS satellite positioning.
- Three-component strong-motion accelerographs installed in Shetland, Edinburgh and Keyworth networks.
- Five strong-motion stations upgraded to allow remote calibration.
- Final report to EU submitted as coordinator of 10-country Transfrontier data exchange project.
- Nox sensor and improved display software to enhance environmental monitoring capability.

- Shock gun source assessed for multicomponent survey capability.
- Analysis of near-offset VSP to demonstrate potential for reservoir monitoring.
- Innovative sub-basalt imaging technique developed using converted shear-waves.
- Anomalous observed waves in reservoirs modelled in terms of faults/large fractures.
- 29 Publications in international peer-reviewed literature in 1996/97.
- New co-funding of £180k pa secured from oil industry for multicomponent seismology.
- Co-funded contract for multicomponent seafloor data analysis initiated with Edinburgh University.

MINERALS AND GEOCHEMICAL SURVEYS

C1 — Geochemical Surveys
Geochemical Baseline Survey Of The Environment (G-BASE)

- Regional geochemistry of north-east England in press.
- Completion of sampling in Humber–Trent area.
- Collection of urban soils in Sheffield and Doncaster.
- Production and release of iterative multimedia CD-ROM, Discovering geology: The Lake District.
- Substantial progress on the interpretation of geochemical images for Regional geochemistry of parts of north-west England and North Wales.
- Hydrogeochemistry database and atlas of Wales, the Welsh Borders and part of the west Midlands.
  — All single-element and single-ion maps prepared.
  — Production of additional value-added products.
  — Preparation of some of the text and maps for the atlas.
- Environmental Survey of Northern Ireland (ESNI):
  — Report on the area sampled in 1995.
  — Completion of sampling of area agreed between DoE/DED/GSNI and BGS.
  — Release of data for area sampled in 1994/95.
- Global geochemical mapping:
  — Publication of The Forum of European Geological Surveys Geochemistry Task Group 1994–1996 Report.
  — Compilation of the FOREGS Geochemistry Inventory as a contribution to the IUGS/IAGC Working Group on Global Geochemical Baselines.

Natural Environmental Radioactivity Survey (NERS)

- Completion of radon-potential and gamma-ray exposure maps of the Liverpool Bay sheet. As they form the model for

future sheets they are being externally reviewed and will then be revised and released.
- Development of a streamlined database design for the Lake District data; appraisal of GIS requirements; and a start on familiarization with the chosen GIS platform.
- Data acquisition for the Lake District, including extensive use of NIREX data.
- Back-calibration of NIREX airborne radiometric survey data against a set of new ground gamma-ray spectrometer measurements.
- Completion of radon-in-soil-gas. measurements for the Lake District for mapped geological units where there are insufficient house radon measurements.
- Classification of geological radon potential for the Lake District, based on analysis of NRPB house radon data and new and existing soil-gas measurements.
- Processing, interpretation and compilation of the data for the Lake District gamma radiation map, now nearly complete.

Development Of Capability In Analytical Chemistry

- Good progress with the North Sea Gas Atlas, which is co-funded by the CEC and industry. The gas composition database was finalized at the end of July, and all maps (15 geological and 21 gas distribution) have now been sent to the co-ordinators (NITG-TNO) for compiling.
- Development of a new fast and reliable method for the determination of halides in crystalline rocks; it has been validated by the analysis of CRMs, and by comparison with an independent method.
- Application of LAMP-ICP-MS to the analysis of fish otoliths in collaboration with CSIRO, Australia; a scoping study was undertaken to extend the technique to examine trace-metal contents of cold-water corals in advance of the start of the MIME project on environmental impacts from oil/gas industry activities. This latter project is to be carried out in collaboration with SAMS. Work continued on the accuracy of analysis of fluid inclusions by LAMP-ICP-MS through exchange visits with CSIC, Barcelona.
- Development of a routine method for the extraction of mercury from both geological and biological matrices is continuing.
- Investigation of the use of a wax and styrene co-polymer binder as an alternative to Elvacite in the preparation of pressed powder pellets for XRF analysis shows that the new binder makes significantly more robust, higher quality, dust-free pellets than Elvacite, and sample preparation time is reduced. The new methods will be implemented as part of ARGG and SPF NAMAS Technical Procedures. A new method for mounting standards into 36 millimetre rings has been developed,

and a set of 52 single element standards consisting of ~1000ppm in SiO2 has been completed.
- Development of chemometric data processing for the interpretation of geochemical and environmental datasets has led to a novel approach to the measurement of trace element distributions in soils and sediments using non-specific extraction and chemometric data-processing.
- Development of optimum dissolution techniques for the analysis of a range of materials by ICP-AES in order to balance the loss of volatile elements against adequate attack of resistate minerals continued. Calibrations were improved to accommodate calcium-rich samples such as cements, marine sediments and flue-gas desulphurization products.
- The extraction and determination of 16 polycyclic aromatic hydrocarbons in contaminated soils and waters by two independent techniques was tested by participation in the Contest scheme. It showed that BGS data obtained by HPLC are significantly better those obtained by some other laboratories using alternative techniques.
- As part or the requirements for NAMAS accreditation, work is continuing on the development of methods to demonstrate the uncertainty of measurement in analytical methods.
- The LIMS system was upgraded to Version 2.0, which is Windows-based. Software has been written to facilitate automated customer sample numbering. Some new data tables have been added and screens have been redesigned to allow easier access. A start was made on the production of User Manuals.

C2 — Mineral Resources

Minerals GIS on-line (MINGOL)

- Completion of demonstration mineral-exploration-information GIS for Britain, including MRP and MEIGA areas.
- Draft report on GIS development for the Lake District 1:250 000 sheet.
- Collection of mineral-deposit data for the Lake District 1:250 000 sheet.
- Datasets of coal licences for South Wales (opencast and deep mined) and mineral planning permissions for Cornwall and South Wales, now available in MINGOL. These form part of the DoE Mineral Resource Planning Map series.
- Interim report on UK trade data.
- Metallogenic Map, published April 1996.
- Mineral Resources of Britain publication:
  — Five chapters complete in draft form: Limestone, Titanium, Kaolin, Ball Clay, Marine sand and gravel aggregates.
  — Overview chapter on mineral

legislation and planning completed in draft form.
— Format, content and data requirements defined.
- Initial specification for a Coal Resources Map of Britain. The Coal Authority was successfully approached for financial support, and the map will be produced as a co-funded project in 1997/98.

Metallogenic Studies (Sedimentary Basins)

- Basin evolution, fluid movement and mineral resources in a Permo-Triassic setting: the Cheshire Basin, now available as a restricted high-cost (£1000) report.
- Ore deposit models and regional exploration criteria for buried carbonate-hosted mineral deposits: a multidisciplinary study in northern England, formerly prepared as a confidential report, now revised, updated, and ready to be prepared for publication.
- Initial report on analyses for joint BGS-NIGL isotopic studies of the Pennine orefields. It is now proposed to draw all this work together for publication.
- Diagrams for Multidataset analysis for the development of metallogenic/economic models and exploration criteria for gold deposits in western Europe are being revised to publication standard. Internal review of the text is in progress.

Palaeofluid Flow In Relation To Resource Development

- Successful completion of a British Council funded research project to compare and contrast laser ablation ICP-MS and cryogenic XRF for the chemical analysis of brine inclusions in halite.
- Initiation of laser ablation ICP-MS study of magmatic-hydrothermal ore fluids using material provided by industrial sponsor (co-funded). Preliminary data confirm the spectacular chemical diversity of fluids from inclusions with apparent similar morphological characteristics. Early exciting conclusions include: strong redox control on concentration of Cu in porphyry copper deposits; role of hydrothermal overprinting in PGE enrichment in magmatic segregation sulphide deposits.
- Completion of EC-funded study of the genesis of the Reocin lead-zinc deposit, Spain. Report and data to be published pending scientific assessment by technical advisors to Brussels.
- One popular publication, highlighting topical aspects of IMP research, for the Royal Society of Chemistry.

C3 — Development of Capability In Mineral Sciences

During the financial year 1996/97, this project was designed as a set of five self-contained sub-projects. These were intended to address future requirements and opportunities arising from the Core Programme (hydrocarbons related techniques; new rock classification scheme; zircon screening), mineral resource evaluation (electron microprobe applications) and the environmental sector (SEM applications; mine waste treatment). Each of these was successful and completed to schedule.

- Application areas for the new SEM–CL for detailed studies of diagenetic cements and fracture mineralization:
  — Completion of initial phase of calibrations, testing and establishment of operating procedures of the new LEO SEM.
  — Examination of new applications in relation to authentication of amethyst gemstones, screening of zonation in zircon crystals intended for U-Pb dating and imaging of fine structure in diseased human soft tissues.
  — Further development and testing of Kontron image-analysis applications of the SEM for automated modal mineralogy and particle characterisation, resulting in current commercial work in relation to the hydrocarbons industry.
  — Issue of formal Operating Procedures for the SEM now awaiting results of the ongoing BGS QA-Audit.
- Application areas for the electron microprobe:
  — Consolidation of a reference library of microchemical zonation patterns in gold grains in relation to source area and mode of origin.
  — A relational database has been designed, built (MS Access) and provided with a test dataset. When populated, this will provide an archive of BGS and other (published) international data on gold and other precious metal chemistry and mineralogy as a resource for further exploration and sourcing investigations.
- Relationships between different depth/maturity indices for sedimentary sequences:
  — Cross-correlations have been established between illite crystallite thickness in mudrocks and other maturity indices, notably vitrinite reflectance, in relation to depth of burial in deep sedimentary sequences in different tectonic regimes.
  — The Portable InfraRed Mineral Analyser (PIMA) was successfully tested and calibrated for characterisation of clays and carbonate cements in drillcore samples from the Winterbourne–Newton deep Mesozoic borehole.
- BGS petrological classification scheme
  — The igneous component of the new scheme to be completed under this project, and contributions by other groups dealing with metamorphic and superficial rocks have also been completed: that for sedimentary rocks is almost finished. The scheme is thus ready for corporate adoption in BGS.
- Mineral Processing procedures:
  — Processing procedures for remedial treatment of heavy-metal contaminated mine waste have been tested using samples of dump material from the Leadhills mining area, Southern Scotland. Laboratory beneficiation and chemical analysis has been completed and a detailed report is in preparation.

C4 — Divisional Databases

Databases And Software Development

- Geochemistry Database:
  — Completion of data and program transfer from VAX to UNIX system.
  — Access Client-Server front end completed and documented.
  — Loading and validation of new MRP and G-BASE data.
  — Loading major lithogeochemical datasets completed.
- British Rocks Database:
  — Design of BritRocks database completed.
  — All data converted from VAX Petmin database to new BritRocks database.
  — Access front-end written.
  — Documentation completed.
- Training:
  — Training on new BritRocks database given to users.
  — Access training given to more staff in Division and BGS.
  — Database–GIS links developed and being improved.

HYDROGEOLOGICAL & GEOTECHNICAL SURVEYS

D1 — National Groundwater Survey

Chalk Aquifer Regional Studies

- Hydrogeology of the Chalk of South Downs: publication returned after PB review and will be published after amendment in 1997–98.
- Hydrogeology of Yorkshire Chalk: contributions and co-funded research completed, final draft planned for completion in 1997–98.

Chalk Aquifer Process Research

Core research activities which have attracted co-funding are:
- Tracer Test Manual: due for publication in September 1997 (EA).
- Baseline Hydrogeochemical Survey: sampling completed (EA).
- Nitrate Trends in Groundwater in Yorkshire Chalk: completed (Yorkshire Water).
- Decision Support System for Lincolnshire Chalk: MSc completed.

- Effect of Old Landfills on Chalk Groundwater Quality (EA); site investigation work carried out at Thriplow site, written up as BGS Technical Report and recommendations for future work accepted; contaminant plume from the landfill lies within 10 metres of the water-table, evidence of chloride pulses in monitoring wells suggests seasonal release of leachate.

National Aquifer Properties Manual

- EA/BGS co-funding of Major Aquifer Properties Manual publication eventually agreed and publication will now be in 1997.
- Initial data collection exercise has started for Minor Aquifer Properties Manual.

National Groundwater Archive

- Amalgamation of groundwater records and digitization of index has progressed well; injection of funding in 1997–98 should ensure completion.
- Enquiry Service responded to a total of 1300 enquiries, an increase of 10 per cent on last year.
- IH-BGS monthly summaries of surface and groundwater resources produced on time as well as publication of 1995 Hydrological Data Yearbook.

Upland Aquifer Studies

- Co-funding from SEPA approved to support databasing of Scottish borehole records and revision of major aquifers.
- BGS Technical Report on Sr isotope study in the Plynlimon catchment.
- Hydrogeochemical Processes in Uplands Catchment: publication delayed into 1997.

D2 — Hydrogeological Formation Properties and Hazards

Hydrogeology of Clay Aquitards

- Pilot 1:50 000 drift classification maps and 3 EA Technical Reports have been written; a monograph on Clay-with-Flints has been produced for BGS publication.
- Clay Thermal Analogue Project (EC): possible analogue sites in Northern Skye have been identified and analysed; BGS staff have visited and advised on main project site in Italy and BGS has received samples from analogue sites in Italy and France for pore fluid extraction/analysis and vitrinite reflectance studies.
- Gas Migration in Argillaceous Rocks (EC): impacts of gas migration pathways on the hydraulic properties have been examined; application of linear elastic fracture mechanics and the Griffith criterion for extensile crack propagation to gas migration have been explored, and investigations on the capacity for pathway re-sealing made; the development of a new apparatus using acoustic emissions to examine the details of intermittent flow has been initiated.

Engineering Behaviour of British Rock and Soil Formations

- Negotiations with the CIRIA for co-funding of this programme are continuing but protracted because of funding difficulties.
- National geotechnical database and geotechnical/mineralogical testing of selected samples of Mercia Mudstone completed, but first draft of monograph delayed to incorporate additional material from commercial contracts.
- Report on Mercia Mudstone of Middlesborough area completed by an Msc student at Newcastle University supported by the project.
- A literature search for the Lambeth Group has been completed, but sampling/testing programme delayed awaiting core from commercial site investigation borehole.
- A formal collaborative project on potentially collapsing soils (loess/brickearth) has been agreed with Nottingham Trent University, which will lead to a joint monograph on UK Potentially-Collapsing Soils.
- Papers on the Brickearth of Essex, the Sneinton Formation, the Coal Measures and the Claygate & Bagshot Beds have been accepted for publication in the Quarterly Journal of Engineering Geology and in Engineering Geology.
- An assessment of the use of indirect methods (including thermal imagery) for the detection of mineshafts has commenced with a BGS Technical Report completed, and a presentation made to the Edinburgh Geological Society on secondary seismic hazards.
- Draft engineering geology and geohazard maps of the UK have been completed in collaboration with the University of Plymouth.

D3 — Technology Foresight and Capability Development

Development of Hydrogeological Capability

- The IH-BGS co-funded study of the Transport and Fate of Pesticides continued: a second interim report was published in October 1996 and plans for future work agreed. The current main conclusion of the work is that degradation is rapid in the soil zone but slow in the unsaturated zone of the Chalk, and by-pass flow is therefore key to groundwater pollution and understanding this process is vital.
- PALAEAUX: 3 plenary meetings have been held in Brighton, Tenerife and Avignon involving 9 country partners. Interactive geochemical, hydrogeological and climatic studies have been initiated in 14 European coastal areas with contrasting sedimentary environments, representing the spectrum of palaeohydrogeological conditions from glacial stationary front environments to island environments affected only by sea level change. Two documents — background and description of study areas and first annual report were prepared.
- The co-funded study of the potential for ASR in Britain initiated in September 1996 has progressed, under guidance of the Steering Committee, resulting in the development of an assessment strategy, survey of available data and a seminar in February 1997 attended by researchers, suppliers, regulators and consultants.

Development of Geosphere Waste Containment Capability

- Predicting Potential for Natural Attenuation (EC): major sampling campaign completed and good inter-laboratory comparison has been achieved between partners, initial evaluation of field data suggests redox zonation in the pollution plume at the Triassic Sandstone site with the presence of metabolites and active bacteria providing support for natural biodegradation reactions and laboratory microcosm experiments have confirmed potential.
- A generic review report has been produced on Fluid Flow in Faults and Fractures.
- A new BGS code (BUGSE) for modelling microbe growth rates in groundwater has been produced.
- An experimental field array of boreholes has been drilled and instrumented in the Mercia Mudstone on the Keyworth site for in-situ gas injection experiments.

Development of Geotechnical Capability

- Development of Best-Practice for Engineering Geophysics: co-funded collaboration with the CIRIA and the Geological Society to produce a new guide on the application of engineering geophysics; 3 presentations made at national seminars and 5 articles published in 'Ground Engineering'.
- Demonstration of Electro-Kinetic Seismic Method for 2-D Distribution of Subsurface Permeability: BGS Technical Reports on the theory and field experiments have been written, with presentation at a Geological Society meeting.
- A BGS Technical Report has been completed on the use of geophysical methods in the assessment and remediation of contaminated land with presentation at a Geological Society meeting.
- Development of 3-D Resistivity Techniques for Subsurface Imaging and Prediction of Physical Properties. Two BGS Technical Reports have been

completed and demonstration of the impact of fine-scale geological structure on the assessment of mass properties using in-situ and core micro-resistivity imaging, in collaboration with two oil companies and Leicester University.

- A mini-pressuremeter for measuring the tensile strength of weak rocks and safer equipment to determine the shrinkage limit of clay soils have been developed in collaboration with Leeds University.

D4 — Urban Environmental Survey

- A methodology for investigating urban areas has been proven and the geographical information system WOLGIS and CD-ROM of databases are available for the Wolverhampton area.
- BGS Technical Reports have been produced on *Wolverhampton Urban Environmental Survey: an integrated geoscientific case study*, and *Urban Environmental Survey Project: an economic perspective*, the latter providing a cost-benefit analysis of urban geoscience.
- A report on the application of risk analysis to geoscientific data in the urban environment has been prepared under subcontract at Nottingham Trent University.
- A BGS Technical Report assessing the potential impact of Cd and As soil contaminants on the Triassic aquifer in wolverhampton has been drafted.

NATIONAL GEOSCIENCE INFORMATION SERVICE

Income from the sale of printed material fell slightly due to the temporary closure of the London Information Office and the Earth Galleries. The value of chargeable enquiries rose by 10 per cent. The number of borehole records awaiting registration was reduced by 26 per cent. The output of new printed 1:50 000-scale maps reached a new high. A new Regional Guide was published. Memoir output dropped but is expected to rise substantially next year as the 1993/94 and 1994/95 submission bulge passes through. A good number of new Popular Publications was released to a generally warm reception. Migration from the VAX to a distributed system was completed at Keyworth.

F1 — Information Services

- National retail network expanded to 58 approved suppliers and 8 wholesalers.
- New Regional Catalogue of BGS Maps and Books produced.
- First two Value Added Reseller Agreements concluded.
- Merger of Central and Library Enquiry Desks; 16 per cent increase in enquiries handled.

- Borehole registration backlog reduced by 26 per cent.
- British borehole Catalogue CD-ROM published through GeoInformation International.
- Mine plan registration project completed.
- Release of Geosystems CD-ROM incorporating BGS Library holdings.
- First phase of data capture completed for index to geological photograph collection.

F2 — Information Systems

- VAX migration at Keyworth completed and VAX cluster decommissioned.
- VAX migration at Edinburgh on schedule for completion 12 months after Keyworth.
- EU co-funded GEIXS contract awarded.
- MARS replacement software delivered.
- Beta-testing PC Geoscience Data System successfully completed.
- BGS Web Server accessed by external users 200 000 times during year.
- Pilot NT server project successfully completed and implementation report delivered.
- Disentanglement from NCS local services completed.
- Completion of IT into Everything study and installation of final phase of 150+ new (VAX replacement) PCs.

F3 — Publication Services

Map Production

- Twenty-nine new 1:50 000-scale maps completed to advance copy release.
- Thirty-one new maps printed, a record high.
- Population of the 1:10 000-scale digital map database continued with 74 sheets approved for release.
- New integrated digital map production system developed, combining the best features of the existing 1:10 000 and 1:50 000-scale systems and based upon a common database standard.

Book Production

- Three new sheet memoirs published (Fortrose, Airdrie and Worcester).
- London and Thames Valley Regional Guide published.

Popular Publications

- First Holiday Geology Guides for London (Trafalgar Square) published with two others (St Paul's and Westminster) nearing completion.
- First Holiday Geology Map published featuring the Isle of Wight with another for the Lake District in preparation.
- Heritage in Stone: Nottingham published.
- Fossil Focus card (Ostracods) published and another (Foraminifera) approaches final proof.

- *Yorkshire rock: a journey through time* published.

Promotions and Public Relations

- Site tours and information provided to the large number of visitors from business, academia and many public bodies.
- Major programme of events organized at Keyworth as BGS contribution to SET'97.
- Eighth and ninth editions of the BGS magazine Earthwise published featuring the International Division and Coastal Zone.
- Press Releases issued regularly on many BGS subjects.

F5 — Divisional Databases

- First phase completed of a country-wide digital database of British lithostratigraphical solid geology at 1: 200 000 scale.

ADDITIONAL CORE ACTIVITIES

Remote Sensing and Image Analysis

- Image Analysis — computer systems re-housed in G block; data conversions completed; international remote sensing conference hosted.
- Digital Photogrammetrical Surveying — series of ImageStation demonstration studies in support of UK Core Programme activities completed.
- PIMA — potential of the Portable Infrared Mineral Analyser reviewed and a preliminary R&D programme developed.
- HYPEX — a proposal for a new NERC EOSTB Thematic Programme on 'Hyperspectral Data Exploitation' prepared and submitted.
- International collaboration — links with the Japan/USA ASTER satellite programme, the Australian ARIES project, and RADARSAT continued and extended.

Director's pump priming

- Funding used by staff devoting more than 75 per cent of their time to commissioned research for the preparation of work for publication; for further development of the publication World Mineral Statistics and to supplement a BGS/University project.

University collaboration

- Fifteen research studentships, including CASE and joint funded, which contributed to the core programme, were supported during the year.
- Twenty seven contracts, let to universities were in operation during the year.